INTRODUCING

MATH!

GRADE 5

ARGOPREP

600 QUESTIONS TO PRACTICE

TEACHER RECOMMENDED

TOPICS COVERED
PRACTICE MAKES PERFECT

- Operations & Algebraic Thinking
- Numbers and Operation in Base Ten
- Fractions
- Measurement and Data
- Geometry

ArgoPrep is one of the leading providers of supplemental educational products and services. We offer affordable and effective test prep solutions to educators, parents and students. Learning should be fun and easy! For that reason, most of our workbooks come with detailed video answer explanations taught by one of our fabulous instructors.

Our goal is to make your life easier, so let us know how we can help you by e-mailing us at:
info@argoprep.com.

ArgoPrep is a recipient of the prestigious **Mom's Choice Award**. ArgoPrep also received the 2019 **Seal of Approval** from Homeschool.com for our award-winning workbooks.

ArgoPrep was awarded the 2019 **National Parenting Products Award** and a **Gold Medal Parent's Choice Award**.

Want an amazing offer from ArgoPrep?

7 DAY ACCESS

to our online premium content at **www.argoprep.com**

Online premium content includes practice quizzes and drills with video explanations and an automatic grading system.

Chat with us live at **www. argoprep.com** for this exclusive offer.

ARGOPREP

TABLE OF CONTENTS

HOW TO USE THE BOOK

Welcome to the **Introducing Math!** series by ArgoPrep.
This workbook is designed to provide you with a comprehensive overview of Grade 5 mathematics.

While working through this workbook, be sure to read the topic overview that will give you a general foundation of the concept. At the end of each chapter, there is a chapter test that will assess how well you understood the topics presented.

This workbook comes with free digital video explanations that you can access on our website. If you are unsure on how to answer a question, we strongly recommend watching the video explanations as it will reinforce the fundamental concepts.

We strive to provide you with an amazing learning experience. If you have any suggestions or need further assistance, don't hesitate to email us at info@argoprep.com or chat with us live on our website at www.argoprep.com

HOW TO WATCH VIDEO EXPLANATIONS
IT IS ABSOLUTELY FREE

Download our app:
ArgoPrep Video Explanations
to access videos on any mobile device or tablet.

OR

Step 1 - Visit our website at: www.argoprep.com/k8
Step 2 - Click on JOIN FOR FREE button located on the top right corner.
Step 3 - Choose the grade level workbook you have.
Step 4 - Sign up as a Learner, Parent or a Teacher.
Step 5 - Register using your email or social networks.
Step 6 - From your dashboard cick on FREE WORKBOOKS EXPLANATION on the left and choose the workbook you have.

OTHER BOOKS BY ARGOPREP

Here are some other test prep workbooks by ArgoPrep you may be interested in. All of our workbooks come equipped with detailed video explanations to make your learning experience a breeze! Visit us at **www.argoprep.com**

COMMON CORE MATH SERIES

 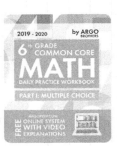  

COMMON CORE ELA SERIES

INTRODUCING MATH!

Introducing Math! by ArgoPrep is an award-winning series created by certified teachers to provide students with high-quality practice problems. Our workbooks include topic overviews with instruction, practice questions, answer explanations along with digital access to video explanations. Practice in confidence - with ArgoPrep!

YOGA MINDFULNESS FOR KIDS

HIGHER LEVEL EXAMS

KIDS SUMMER ACADEMY SERIES

ArgoPrep's **Kids Summer Academy** series helps prevent summer learning loss and gets students ready for their new school year by reinforcing core foundations in math, english and science. Our workbooks also introduce new concepts so students can get a head start and be on top of their game for the new school year!

Meet the ArgoPrep heroes.

Are you ready to go on an incredible adventure and complete your journey with them to become a **SUPER** student?

WATER FIRE

MYSTICAL NINJA

GREEN POISON

FIRESTORM WARRIOR

RAPID NINJA

CAPTAIN ARGO

THUNDER WARRIOR

ADRASTOS THE SUPER WARRIOR

Our **Kids Summer Academy** series by **ArgoPrep** is designed to keep students engaged with fun graphics and activities. Our curriculum is aligned with state standards to help your child prepare for their new school year.

Chapter 1
Operations & Algebraic Thinking

ARGOPREP
STUDY SMARTER, NOT HARDER

Math problems can be written with more than one operation. To solve these more difficult problems, we follow a sequence called the **order of operations**.

Consider the numerical expression $3 + 4 \times 6$

There are two possible solutions to this problem:

$3 + 4 \times 6 = 42$ ✗

If you solve the problem left to right, you get 42. However, that answer is incorrect.

$3 + 4 \times 6 = 27$ ✓

If you solve the problem by multiplying first and then adding, you get 27. This answer is correct.

How do I know which part of the problem to solve first?
The **order of operations** tells you which part of the problem to solve first.

ORDER OF OPERATIONS:

Step One: Calculate operations in grouping symbols first. Grouping symbols include **parentheses**, **brackets** or **braces**. If an expression has more than one grouping symbol, calculate the operations in parentheses first, brackets second, and braces third.

( )	[ ]	{ }
Parentheses	Brackets	Braces

Step Two: Solve **exponents**, including square roots. It's okay if you aren't familiar with these terms yet. We will learn more about them in an upcoming chapter.

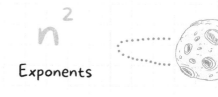

Exponents

Step Three: Multiply and **Divide**. It both multiplication and division appear in an expression, complete the operations in the order they appear.

Multiplication/Division

Step Four: Add and **Subtract**. It both addition and subtraction appear in an expression, complete the operations in the order they appear.

+ —

Addition/Subtraction

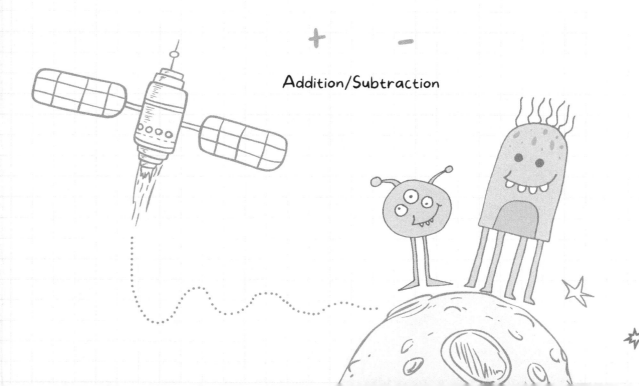

PEMDAS

You can use the acronym PEMDAS to help you remember the order of operations.

P - Parentheses, Brackets, Braces
E - Exponents
MD - Multiplication/Division
AS - Addition/Subtraction

Let's look at another example.

$3 \times [4 + (2 \times 3)]$
$\vee$
$3 \times [4 + 6]$
$\vee$
3×10
$\vee$
30

first calculate the operation in parentheses

next, calculate the operation in brackets

finally, multiply.

$$3 \times [4 + (2 \times 3)] = 30 \checkmark$$

Practice Questions

1. Solve $5 + (3 \times 4)$. Show your work.

SHOW YOUR WORK

2. Which part of the expression should be calculated first? Explain your answer.

$$7 + \{8 \times [12 \div (6 - 3)]\}$$

A. $7 + 8$

B. 8×12

C. $12 \div 6$

D. $6 - 3$

SHOW YOUR WORK

3. Add parentheses to the equation without changing it's value.

$$7 + 8 \times 3 = 45$$

SHOW YOUR WORK

4. Solve $2 \times [6 + (8 - 3)]$. Show your work.

> SHOW YOUR WORK

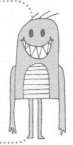

5. Which numerical expression has the same value as $5 + 3 \times (6 + 2)$?

A. $(3 \times 5) - 8$

B. $4 + (5 \times 5)$

C. $6 + (5 \times 6)$

D. $(6 \times 10) + 4$

> SHOW YOUR WORK

6. Which part of the expression below should be calculated first? Explain your answer.

$$3 + \{10 \times [6 + 2 \times (6 - 3) + 12]\}$$

A. 10×6

B. $6 + 2$

C. 2×6

D. $6 - 3$

> SHOW YOUR WORK

16

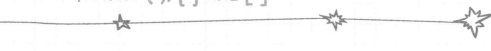
7. Is the following equation true? Explain your answer.

$$(7 - 3) + 6 \times 2 = 20$$

SHOW YOUR WORK

8. Solve $(24 + 6) \div 3$. Show your work.

SHOW YOUR WORK

9. Add parentheses to the equation without changing its value.

$$54 \div 6 - 3 = 6$$

SHOW YOUR WORK

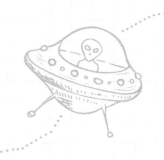

10. Is the following equation true? Explain your answer.

$$6 + 36 \div (3 \times 2) - 3 = 4$$

SHOW YOUR WORK

11. Solve $(7 \times 2) + (9 \times 6)$. Show your work.

SHOW YOUR WORK

12. Is the following equation true? Explain your answer.

$$4 + 8 \times (6 - 4) = 20$$

SHOW YOUR WORK

13. Which numerical expression has the same value as [(2 + 8) × 3] + 6

    A. [5 + (8 × 3)] + 6

    B. 2 + [(8 × 3) + 6]

    C. (10 × 3) + 6

    D. 10 × (3 + 6)

SHOW YOUR WORK

14. Solve 8 + [6 × (8 - 6)] ÷ 3. Show your work.

SHOW YOUR WORK

15. Add parentheses to the equation without changing its value.

$$60 ÷ 2 + 6 - 3 = 33$$

SHOW YOUR WORK

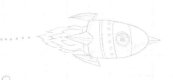

Write Numerical Expressions

We can use what we've learned about the order of operations to write our own numerical expressions. Let's look at an example.

Write an expression for the sum of **28** and **7**, divided by **5**

<u>What we know:</u>

Sum is an addition word   28 + 7
Divided by signals division.   ÷ 5

Listing what we know helps us determine which numbers and operations should be included in the expression. We can see that the expression will include both addition and division.

Next, we need to determine the order or operations.

The problem states that the sum of **28** and **7** is divided by **5**. So, we need to add **28** and **7** before dividing by **5**. We can use parentheses in our expression to ensure addition is calculated first.

The answer is (28 + 7) ÷ 5

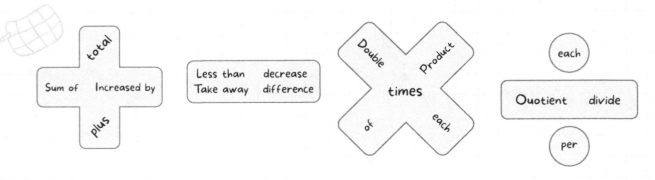

Let's look at another example.

> Lara's garden has two times as many cucumbers as Sarah's garden. Sarah's garden has **6** rows of **3** cucumbers. Write an expression to determine how many cucumbers Lara has in her garden. Do not evaluate the expression.
>
> <u>What we know:</u>
>
> Lara has two times as many cucumbers as Sarah ✓   2 ×
> Sarah has **6** rows of **3** cucumbers ✓   6 × 3

The phrase two times as many signals that this is a comparison problem, which means our expression with include a multiplication. The word of also signals multiplication.

Next, we need to determine the order of operations.

The problem states that Lara's garden has twice as many cucumbers as Sarah's garden. So, we need to calculate the number of cucumbers in Sarah's garden first. Then, we can double it to find the number of cucumbers in Lara's garden.

$(6 × 3) × 2$

Practice Questions

1. Write an expression that represents Add 12 and 4, then divide by 2.

SHOW YOUR WORK

2. Which phrase is represented by the expression 6 × (8 + 2)?

A. 6 times 8, plus 2

B. Add 6 and 8, then multiply by 2

C. The sum of 8 and 2, times 6

D. The product of 8 and 2, times 6

SHOW YOUR WORK

3. Which problem could be solved with the expression 3 × (6 + 9)?

A. Tia hikes 3 trails on Monday. She hikes 6 more trails on Tuesday and 9 more trails on Wednesday. How many trails did she hike in all?

B. Olivia swims 3 times a day. She swims 6 laps with a kickboard and 9 laps without a kickboard. How many laps does she swim each day?

C. Lars has 3 apples. He buys 6 more apples. He eats 9 of his apples. How many apples does Lars have left?

SHOW YOUR WORK

4. Which expression is 10 times as large as the expression 5 + (4 × 8)?

A. 10 × 5 + (4 × 8)

B. 10 + 5 + (4 × 8)

C. 10 + [5 + (4 × 8)]

D. 10 × [5 + (4 × 8)]

SHOW YOUR WORK

5. Marisol is baking cookies for her friend.

- She starts by making **12** cookies

- Her brother eats **3** of the cookies

- Her dad helps her bake triple the number of remaining cookies

Write an expression to show the number of cookies Marisol has for her friend.

SHOW YOUR WORK

6. Write an expression that represents five times the quotient of **6** and **3**.

SHOW YOUR WORK

7. Which phrase is represented by the expression (8 ÷ 2) × 2?

A. The quotient of 8 and 2, doubled

B. The quotient of 8 and 2, tripled

C. 8 divided by 2, quadrupled

D. 2 times 2, divided by 8

SHOW YOUR WORK

8. Ben drinks one glass of milk each day of the week. Albert drinks three times as many glasses of milk each week. Write an expression that represents how many glasses of milk Albert drinks in one week.

SHOW YOUR WORK

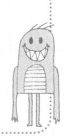

9. Chen is raking leaves.

- He starts by raking 13 piles

- 7 of his piles blow away

- He rakes 10 more piles of leaves

- Half of the remaining piles blow away

Which expression shows the amount of piles Chen had left?

A. (13 - 7) × (10 ÷ 2)

B. 13 - 7 + (10 ÷ 2)

C. [(13 - 7) + 10] ÷ 2

D. 13 - [7 + (10 ÷ 2)]

SHOW YOUR WORK

10. Which phrase represents the expression 9 × (3 + 4)?

A. 9 more than the sum of 3 and 4

B. 9 more than the product of 3 and 4

C. 9 times the product of 3 and 4

D. 9 times 4 more than 3

SHOW YOUR WORK

11. The picture below represents 5 + 9. Draw a picture that represents 4 × (5 + 9)

SHOW YOUR WORK

12. Write an expression that represents the product of 3 times 5 more than 3

SHOW YOUR WORK

13. Write an expression that represents 4 times as large as the expression [(6 + 2) × 3] + 2?

SHOW YOUR WORK

14. Write an expression that represents The sum of 12 and 4, divided in half.

SHOW YOUR WORK

15. Which phrase could represent the expression (9 - 3) × 2

A. Twice as many as the difference between 9 and 3

B. The product of 9 and 3, times 2

C. The quotient of 9 and 3, doubled

D. 9 minus the product of 3 and 2

SHOW YOUR WORK

See "Graphing Points on a Coordinate Plane" before completing this section.

We can use what we know about patterns to complete the chart below.

Point	x Rule: Add 2	y Rule: Add 4	Ordered Pair (x, y)
A	2	4	
B			
C			
D			

For the x-coordinates, we add 2 to each row.

For the y-coordinate, we add 4 to each row.

We list the ordered pairs using a set of parenthesis. Always list the x-coordinate first, then the y-coordinate.

Graphing the Results

Once we've determine the ordered pairs, we can create a visual by plotting the points on a coordinate plane.

x Rule: Add 2	y Rule: Add 4	Ordered Pair (x, y)
2	4	(2, 4)
4	8	(4, 8)
6	12	(6, 12)

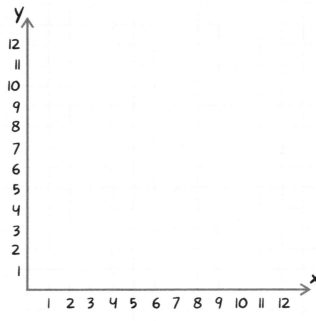

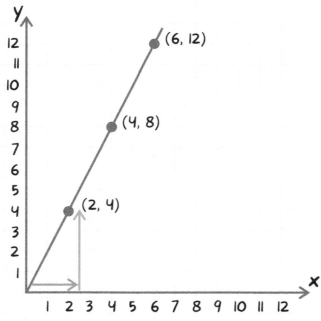

Remember

Travel across the x-axis first.

Then travel up the y-axis.

Use a ruler to connect the points.

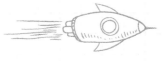

Explaining the Results

The line graph helps us visualize the relationship between the x- and y-coordinates. In this example, the y-coordinate is always twice as large as the x-coordinate. Another way to express the relationship is to say the terms in pattern y are **2** times as much as the terms in pattern x. You could also express the relationship as y = **2** × x

Practice Questions

1. Use the rules to complete the chart below. Describe the relationship between the two sequences.

Sequence 1 Rule: Add 2	Sequence 2: Rule: Add 6
2	6

SHOW YOUR WORK

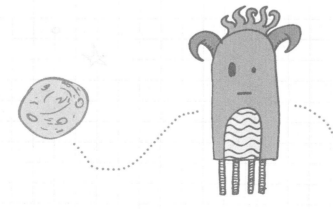

2. Which coordinates represent **2** other points that fall on the line represented in the chart below. Use the graph to show your work.

A. (9, 12) and (15, 18)

B. (9, 12) and (12, 14)

C. (12, 18) and (24, 36)

D. (12, 18) and (18, 21)

Point	x	y
A	0	3
B	3	6
C	6	9

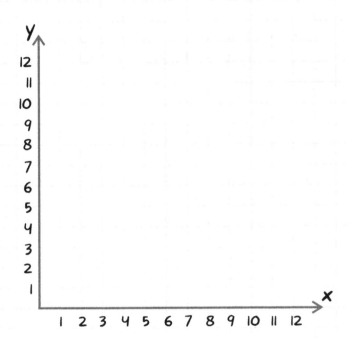

NOTES

3. Complete the table below. Then explain the relationship between the x-coordinates and y-coordinates.

Point	X	Y	(x, y)
A	1	3	(1, 3)
B	3	5	
C	6	8	
D	9	11	

SHOW YOUR WORK

4. Which statement describes the relationship between the two lines shown the graph below.

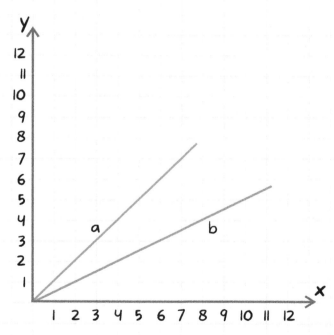

A. Line b is steeper than Line a

B. The y-coordinates in Line a are twice as large as the y-coordinates in Line b

C. Line a and Line b are perpendicular

D. Line a and Line b are parallel

SHOW YOUR WORK

5. How are (1,7) and (7,1) different when plotted on the coordinate plane?

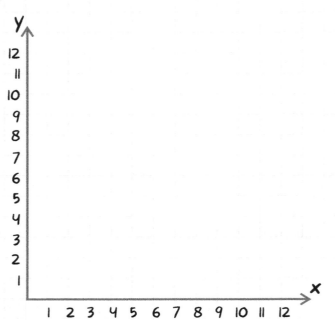

SHOW YOUR WORK

6. What rule is used to get the y values in this chart?

x	y
5	10
7	14
9	18

A. Add 2

B. Subtract 2

C. Multiply by 2

D. Divide by 2

SHOW YOUR WORK

7. Complete the table below.

X	Y	(x,y)
3	9	
5	25	
7		
9		(9, 81)

SHOW YOUR WORK

8. Complete the table for the coordinate plane shown below.

x	y
0	9
2	
4	
6	

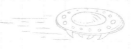

NOTES

9. Complete the chart for the rule Add **2** to x to get y

x	y
5	
7	
9	

SHOW YOUR WORK

10. What rule is used to get the y values in the chart?

x	y
2	5
4	9
6	13

A. Multiply by **2** and subtract **1**

B. Multiply by **2** and add **1**

C. Add **2** and multiply b

D. Add **2** and subtract by **2**

SHOW YOUR WORK

11. The graph below shows y, the total cost in dollars, for x scoops of ice cream.

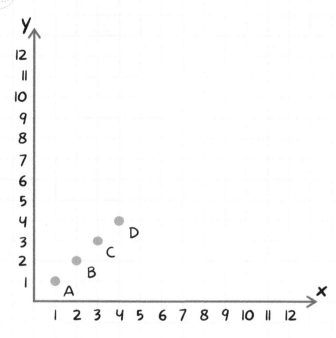

Based on the information in the graph, what would be the total cost for **3** scoops of ice cream?

A. $1

B. $2

C. $3

D. $4

SHOW YOUR WORK

12. Complete the chart for the rule add 1 to the product of 3 and x.

x	y
2	
3	
4	

SHOW YOUR WORK

ARGOPREP

13. Plot the points on the coordinate plane and connect the points. Then complete the chart.

x	y
6	2
7	3
8	4

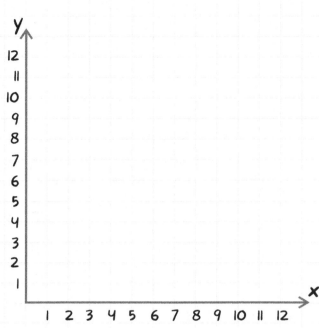

SHOW YOUR WORK

14. Write a rule representing the relationship between the coordinates.

x	y
6	3
8	4
10	5

SHOW YOUR WORK

15. The graph below shows y, the total cost in dollars, for x number of berries. Line s represents strawberries. Line b represents blueberries.

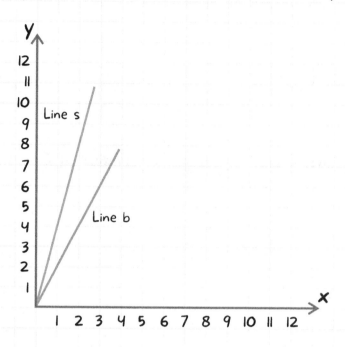

Based on the information in the graph, which type of berry is more expensive? Explain your reasoning.

SHOW YOUR WORK

1. Solve $9 \times [(27 - 19) + 2]$. Show your work.

SHOW YOUR WORK

2. Write an expression that represents Eight fewer than the product of **6** and **3**.

SHOW YOUR WORK

3. Which numerical expression has the same value as $7 + 2 \times [(6 - 3) + 4)]$

A. $9 \times (3 + 4)$

B. $(9 \times 3) + 4$

C. $(2 \times 7) + 7$

D. $2 \times (3 + 4)$

SHOW YOUR WORK

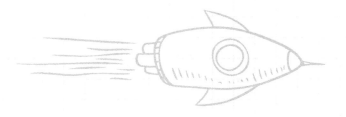

4. What are the rules for the two graphs below?

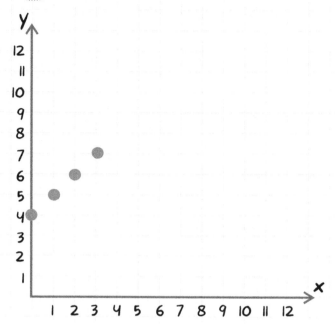

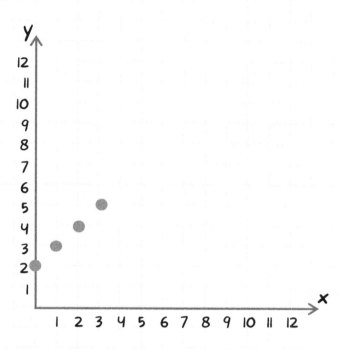

A. 1. First graph: $y = 4 + x$; Second graph $y = 2 + x$

B. 2. First graph: $y = 4 + x$; Second graph $y = 5 + x$

C. 3. First graph: $y = 7 + x$; Second graph $y = 5 + x$

D. 4. First graph: $y = 7 + x$; Second graph $y = 2 + x$

SHOW YOUR WORK

5. How are (3, 4) and (4, 3) different when plotted on a coordinate grid?

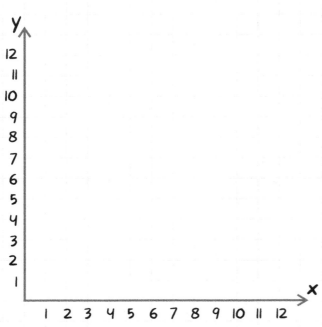

6. Mia is trying to solve the expression below. In which step does she make her first mistake?

$\{2 + [3 + (9 \times 5)]\} \div 2$

Step 1: $\{2 + [3 + (9 \times 5)]\} \div 2$

Step 2: $\{2 + [3 + 45]\} \div 2$

Step 3: $\{2 + 48\} \div 2$

Step 4: $2 + 24$

Answer: $\{2 + [3 + (9 \times 5)]\} \div 2 = 26$

SHOW YOUR WORK

7. Which coordinates represent **2** other points that fall on the line represented in the chart below.

Point	x	y
A	2	4
B	3	6
C	4	8

A. (6, 12) and (12, 14)

B. (6, 12) and (7, 49)

C. (5, 10) and (15, 30)

D. (5, 10) and (6, 21)

SHOW YOUR WORK

8. Solve [(17 - 12) + (22 ÷ 2)] ÷ 4. Show your work.

SHOW YOUR WORK

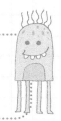

9. The picture below represents **5 + 3**. Draw a picture that represents **(5 + 3) × 3**.

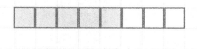

SHOW YOUR WORK

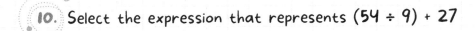

10. Select the expression that represents (54 ÷ 9) + 27

A. The product of 54 and 9 added to 27

B. The quotient of 54 and 9 added to 27

C. 27 plus 9, divided by 54

D. 54 plus 27, divided by 9

SHOW YOUR WORK

Use the graph below for questions 11 - 14

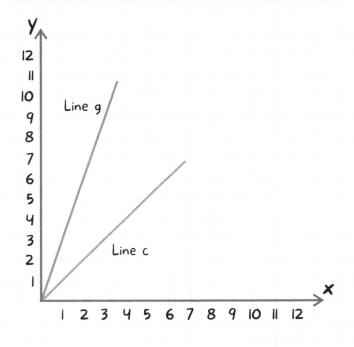

The graph below shows y, the total cost in dollars, for x number of cookies.

Line c represents chocolate chip.

Line g represents ginger snap.

11. Based on the information in the graph, which type of cookie is more expensive? Explain your reasoning.

SHOW YOUR WORK

12. What rule is used to represent line c

A. $y = x + 1$

B. $y = x$

C. $y = x - 1$

D. $y = x \times 1$

SHOW YOUR WORK

13. Write a rule to represent line g.

SHOW YOUR WORK

14. Which statement describes the relationship between line c and line g?

A. The lines are parallel

B. The y-coordinates on line g are three times the size of the y-coordinates on line c

C. The y-coordinates on line c are three times the size of the y-coordinates on line g

D. The lines are equal

SHOW YOUR WORK

15. Suzuna is stacking blocks.

- She starts by stacking 11 blocks

- 3 of her blocks get knocked over

- She adds 12 more blocks to her stack

- Half of the remaining piles blow away

Which expression shows the number of blocks Suzuna had in her stack at the end of the sequence?

A. $[(11 - 3) + 12] - \frac{1}{2}$

B. $11 - [3 + (12 \div 2)]$

C. $[(11 - 3) + 12] \div 2$

D. $11 - 3 + (12 \div 2)$

SHOW YOUR WORK

16. Which problem could be solved with the expression $(4 + 3) \times 7$?

A. Lara eats 4 cookies. Sarah eats 7 times as many cookies. How many cookies do they eat in all?

B. Megan has 4 dolls. She gives 3 away. Her parents give her 7 more dolls. How many does she have left?

C. Pristine spends 4 hours studying math each day. She spends another 3 hours studying social studies each day. How many hours does she study in one week?

SHOW YOUR WORK

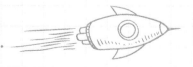

17. Which numerical expression is six times larger than $(29 + 16) \div 9$

A. $(29 + 16) \div 9 \times 6$

B. $(29 + 16) \div (9 \times 6)$

C. $6 \times (29 + 16) \div (9 \times 6)$

D. $[(29 + 16) \div 9] \times 6$

SHOW YOUR WORK

18. Which phrase is represented by the expression $(81 \div 9) \times 3$?

A. The quotient of 81 and 9, doubled

B. The quotient of 81 and 9, tripled

C. 81 divided by 9 times 3

D. The product of 81 and 9, doubled

SHOW YOUR WORK

19. Complete the chart below. What rule is used to get the y values?

x	y	(x,y)
1	6	(1, 6)
2	7	
3	8	

SHOW YOUR WORK

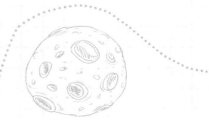

20. Write an expression that represents The sum of **6** and **9**, divided by **3**.

SHOW YOUR WORK

NOTES

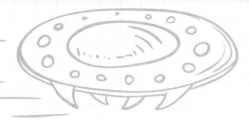

Chapter 2
Numbers & Operations in Base Ten

ARGOPREP
STUDY SMARTER, NOT HARDER

We can use what we know about place value to quickly multiply and divide decimals by 10. Consider the place value chart below. Each digit is 10 times greater than the digit to its right.

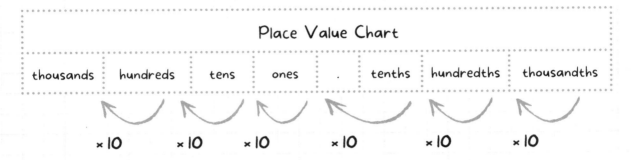

Likewise, each digit is $\frac{1}{10}$ the size of the digit to its left.

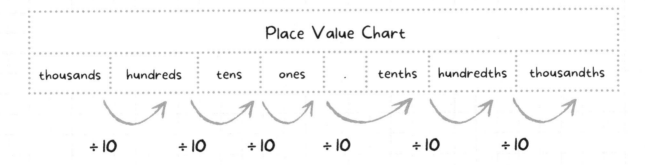

What does this mean?
It means that we can follow a pattern when multiplying or dividing by 10.

Multiplying by 10

We can use the place value chart to multiply by 10. Multiplying by 10 makes a number bigger by shifting the place value to the left. Consider the equation below.

$$362.489 \times 10 =$$

Step 1: Determine the current place value of each digit using the place value chart.

Place Value Chart							
thousands	hundreds	tens	ones		tenths	hundredths	thousandths
	3	6	2	.	4	8	9

Step 2: Shift the place value.

Since we are multiplying by 10, we know we need to shift the place value to the left.

Place Value Chart							
thousands	hundreds	tens	ones		tenths	hundredths	thousandths
3	6	2	4	.	8	9	

Step 3: Analyze how the number changed.

We can see in the place value chart that **362.489** is now written as **3,624.89**.

$$362.489 \times 10 = 3,624.89$$

Dividing decimals by 10

The place value chart can be used to divide decimals by 10 as well. Dividing by 10 makes a number smaller by shifting the place value to the right. Remember that dividing by 10 is the same as multiplying by $\frac{1}{10}$. Let's look at another example.

$$64.28 \div 10$$

The expression could also be expressed as $64.28 \times \frac{1}{10}$

Step 1: Determine the current place value of each digit.

Place Value Chart							
thousands	hundreds	tens	ones		tenths	hundredths	thousandths
		6	4	.	2	8	

Step 2: Shift the place value.

Since we are dividing by 10, we know we need to shift the place value to the right.

Place Value Chart							
thousands	hundreds	tens	ones		tenths	hundredths	thousandths
			6	.	4	2	8

Step 3: Analyze how the number changed.

We can see in the place value chart that 64.28 is now written as 6.428.

$64.28 \div 10 = 6.428$ **or** $64.28 \times \frac{1}{10} = 6.428$

Practice Questions

1. $134 \times \frac{1}{10} =$

A. 1,340

B. 13.4

C. 1.34

D. .134

SHOW YOUR WORK

2. The value of 9 in 1,590

A. 9 tenths

B. 9 tens

C. 9 hundreds

D. 9 hundredths

SHOW YOUR WORK

3. 5 hundreds × 10 = ?

A. 5 tens

B. 5 hundreds

C. 5 thousands

D. 5 hundredths

SHOW YOUR WORK

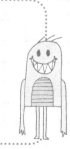

4. The value of 3 in 17.3 is ___ times the value of the 6 in 16.2.

A. $\frac{1}{10}$

B. 2

C. 10

D. 100

SHOW YOUR WORK

5. 3 hundredths × $\frac{1}{10}$ =

A. 3 thousandths

B. 3 tenths

C. 3 tens

D. 3 thousands

SHOW YOUR WORK

6. The value of 4 in 12.43 is ___ times the value of the 8 in 13.28.

A. $\frac{1}{10}$

B. 2

C. 10

D. 100

SHOW YOUR WORK

7. 7 tens ÷ 10 =

A. 7 hundredths

B. 7 tenths

C. 7 ones

D. 7 hundreds

SHOW YOUR WORK

8. Find the product of **3,450 × 10**. Explain your answer.

SHOW YOUR WORK

9. What is the value of the digit in the hundreds place of the number **7,468.87?**

A. 400

B. 4

C. 700

D. 7

SHOW YOUR WORK

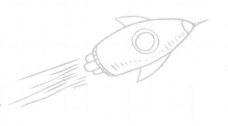

10. Find the quotient of 18,726 ÷ 10. Explain your answer.

SHOW YOUR WORK

NOTES

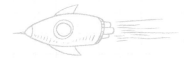

Place Value and Powers of Ten

We know that multiplying by 10 makes a number bigger by shifting the place value to the left. We also know that dividing by 10 makes a number smaller by shifting the place value to the right. But what happens when we multiply or divide by a power of 10?

Consider the expression below.

$$1.872 \times 10^3$$

← The exponent indicates how far the place value is shifting

The operation indicates the direction to shift the place value

Step One: Determine the place value for the original number

Place Value Chart							
thousands	hundreds	tens	ones		tenths	hundredths	thousandths
			1	.	8	7	2

Step Two: Determine the direction the place value will shift. Since we are multiplying, we know we need to move the place value to the left.

Step Three: Determine the number of places to shift. The exponent is 3. So, we need to shift the place value three times.

Place Value Chart							
thousands	hundreds	tens	ones		tenths	hundredths	thousandths
1	8	7	2	.			

$$1.872 \times 10^3 = 1,872$$

Practice Questions

1. $9.7 \times 10^1 =$

   A. .097

   B. .97

   C. 97

   D. 970

SHOW YOUR WORK

2. What is another way to write $543.25 \div 10^2$?

   A. 5,4325

   B. 5.4325

   C. 54.325

   D. .54325

SHOW YOUR WORK

3. What is another way to write 1.27×10^2?

A. .0127

B. .127

C. 12.7

D. 127

SHOW YOUR WORK

4. $29.3 \times 10^3 =$

A. 293

B. 2,930

C. 29,300

D. 293,000

SHOW YOUR WORK

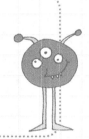

5. Which of the following is equivalent to 2×10^4?

A. 2×400

B. $2 \times 10,000$

C. 2×40

D. 20^4

SHOW YOUR WORK

6. $6.87 \div 10^3 =$

A. 687

B. .687

C. .0687

D. .00687

SHOW YOUR WORK

7. Which of the following is equivalent to 100?

A. 10×2

B. 10×10

C. 10^3

SHOW YOUR WORK

8. $7.2 \times 10^6 =$

SHOW YOUR WORK

9. Which of the following is equivalent to 10^4?

A. 100

B. 1,000

C. $10 \times 10 \times 10$

D. $10 \times 10 \times 10 \times 10$

SHOW YOUR WORK

10. Which of the following is equivalent to 6×10^2?

A. 6×20

B. 6×100

C. $6 \times 1,000$

SHOW YOUR WORK

NOTES

Read, write, and compare decimals to thousandths

Numbers can be written in a variety of ways. We already know how to write whole numbers using expanded and word form. Rewriting decimals can be a bit trickier.

Consider the number 15.375

The number is already written in standard form. We want to rewrite it in both expanded and word form.

Expanded Form

To write a decimal in expanded form, we multiply each digit by its place value. It can be helpful to use the place value chart as a reference.

Place Value Chart							
thousands	hundreds	tens	ones		tenths	hundredths	thousandths
		1	5	.	3	7	5

$$(1 \times 10) + (5 \times 1) + \quad (3 \times \frac{1}{10}) + (7 \times \frac{1}{100}) + (5 \times \frac{1}{1000})$$

$$15.375 = (1 \times 10) + (5 \times 1) + (3 \times \frac{1}{10}) + (7 \times \frac{1}{100}) + (5 \times \frac{1}{1000})$$

Word Form

When we write a decimal in word form, we use the word "and" to represent the decimal. We write everything before the decimal as a whole number. We use the place value of the last decimal number to express the numbers after the decimal. Let's look at 15.375 again.

Place Value Chart

thousands	hundreds	tens	ones		tenths	hundredths	**thousandths**
		1	5	.	3	7	5

Fifteen   and   three hundred seventy-five thousandths

Comparing two decimals

Once we understand the meaning of each digit, we can compare decimals to one another using the symbols below.

> **>**
greater than

=
equal to

<
less than

Let's try comparing two decimals.

0.45 ___ .047

Step 1: Look at place value for each number

0.457

Place Value Chart

thousands	hundreds	tens	ones		tenths	**hundredths**	thousandths
			0	.	4	5	

.047

Place Value Chart

thousands	hundreds	tens	ones		tenths	hundredths	thousandths
				.	0	4	7

Step 2: Compare the two numbers

We can see just by looking at the place value chart that **0.45** is greater than **.047** because we know that the tenths place is **10** times greater than the hundredths place.

Step 3: Insert the symbol

Look back at the comparison statement. We want the statement to read, **0.45** is greater than **.047**. So, we insert the greater than symbol.

0.45 > .047

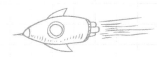

Practice Questions

1. Write the number 95.321 in expanded form.

SHOW YOUR WORK

2. 27.5 =

A. $(2 \times 10) + (7 \times 1) + (5 \times \frac{1}{10})$

B. $(2 \times 10) + (7 \times 1) + (5 \times \frac{1}{100})$

C. $(2 \times 10) + (7 \times 1) + (5 \times 10)$

SHOW YOUR WORK

3. 3.26 ___ 3.62

A. >

B. <

C. =

SHOW YOUR WORK

4. Write the number 7.869 in expanded form

A. $(7 \times 10) + (8 \times 1) + (6 \times \frac{1}{100}) + (9 \times \frac{1}{1000})$

B. $(7 \times 1) + (8 \times 1) + (6 \times \frac{1}{100}) + (9 \frac{1}{1000})$

C. $(7 \times 1) + (8 \times \frac{1}{10}) + (6 \times \frac{1}{100}) + (9 \times \frac{1}{1000})$

SHOW YOUR WORK

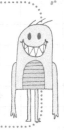

5. 0.80 ___ 0.8

A. >

B. <

C. =

SHOW YOUR WORK

6. Which expression has the greatest value?

A. three hundredths

B. thirty hundredths

C. three hundred thirty thousandths

SHOW YOUR WORK

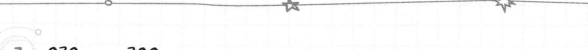
7. .030 ___ .300

    A. >

    B. <

    C. =

    SHOW YOUR WORK

8. What number is equivalent to the expanded form shown below?

    $$(8 \times 10) + (4 \times \frac{1}{10}) + (6 \times \frac{1}{100}) + (4 \times \frac{1}{1000})$$

    A. 0.8464

    B. 80.464

    C. 8.464

    SHOW YOUR WORK

9. 5 tenths ___ 5 ones

    A. >

    B. <

    C. =

    SHOW YOUR WORK

10. Which answer equivalent to 1,000 + 300 + 40 + 5

A. (1 × 1,000) + (3 × 100) + (45 × tens)

B. 1 thousands + 3 hundreds + 40 tens + 5 ones

C. 1,345

SHOW YOUR WORK

11. 3 hundredths ___ 30

A. >

B. <

C. =

SHOW YOUR WORK

12. Write the number 82.675 in expanded form.

SHOW YOUR WORK

13. Masa lives 10.81 miles from school. Facundo lives 10.752 miles from school. Which comparison statement represents the distances they live from school?

A. 10.81 > 10.752

B. 10.81 < 10.752

C. 10.81 = 10.752

SHOW YOUR WORK

14. What number is equivalent to **534.6**

A. 5 hundreds + 3 tens + 4 ones + 6 oneths

B. $(5 \times 100) + (34 \times 10) + (4 \times 1) + (6 \times \frac{1}{10})$

C. Five hundred thirty-four and six tenths

SHOW YOUR WORK

15. Write the number **6.373** in expanded form.

SHOW YOUR WORK

16. Albert rode his bike **2.753** miles on Saturday. Ben rode his bike **2.76** miles. Which comparison statement represents the distances they biked?

A. 2.753 > 2.76

B. 2.753 < 2.76

C. 2.753 = 2.76

SHOW YOUR WORK

17. 543.65 ___ 54.98

A. >

B. <

C. =

SHOW YOUR WORK

18. ___ > 3.14

A. 03.14

B. 30.14

C. 3.140

SHOW YOUR WORK

19. 0.34 ____ .340

A. >

B. <

C. =

SHOW YOUR WORK

20. What number is equivalent to the expanded form shown below?

$$(3 \times 100) + (6 \times 1) + (1 \times \frac{1}{10}) + (9 \times \frac{1}{100})$$

A. 306.19

B. 311.9

C. 301.019

SHOW YOUR WORK

NOTES

Rounding decimals

There are times when we need to round numbers in order to make them easier to use. We know how to round whole numbers, but we also need to be able to round decimals. Consider the problem below.

Round **25.706** to the nearest hundredth.

We round decimals the same way we round whole numbers. You just need to be sure you are looking at the correct digit. It can be helpful to use the place value chart.

Step 1: Identify the digit that needs to be rounded.
In this case, it's the hundredths place.

Place Value Chart							
thousands	hundreds	tens	ones		tenths	hundredths	**thousandths**
		2	5	.	7	0	6

Step 2: Look at the number to the right of the digit that needs to be rounded. In this case, we are looking at the thousandths place.

Step 3: Determine if you need to round up or down.
If the number to the right is greater than (or equal to) **5**, round up. If the number is less than **5**, round down. In this case, we round up.

25.710

Practice Questions

1. Round **2.569** to the nearest hundredth

> SHOW YOUR WORK

2. Which number is equivalent to **84** when rounded to the nearest ones place?

A. 83.17

B. 83.63

C. 84.70

D. 84.89

> SHOW YOUR WORK

3. Round **6.7534** to the nearest thousandth

> SHOW YOUR WORK

4. What is **2.57** rounded to the nearest whole number?

A. 2

B. 3

C. 2.6

D. 2.5

SHOW YOUR WORK

5. Round **5.75** to the nearest tenth

SHOW YOUR WORK

6. Which number is **not** equivalent to **97** when rounded to the nearest whole number?

A. 97.01

B. 97.05

C. 96.90

D. 96.09

SHOW YOUR WORK

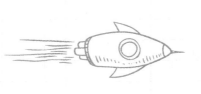

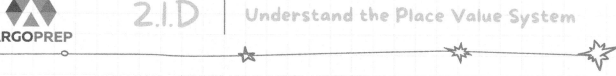

7. Round **298.67** to the nearest ten

SHOW YOUR WORK

8. Round **8.897** to the nearest hundredth

SHOW YOUR WORK

9. Which number is **not** equivalent to **24.5** when rounded to the nearest tenth?

A. 24.05

B. 24.49

C. 24.45

D. 24.52

SHOW YOUR WORK

10. Round **768.756** to the nearest hundredth

SHOW YOUR WORK

We can use the standard algorithm to multiply whole numbers with more than one digit.

Let's look at an example.

$$132 \times 14$$

These are big numbers. They can be intimidating at first, but there's an algorithm to help.

The standard algorithm

132 × 14

```
  132        132
× 10       ×  4
─────      ─────
1,320       528
        +
```

1848

Step 1: Break the smaller number into partial products that are easier to handle.

Step 2: Multiply the larger number by the partial products.

Step 3: Use addition to put the partial products back together.

NOTES

Practice Questions

1. 67 × 30 = ___ Show your work.

> SHOW YOUR WORK

2. There are **32** dozen cupcakes at the party. How many cupcakes are there in all?

A. 64

B. 320

C. 364

D. 384

> SHOW YOUR WORK

3. 28 × 156 = ___ Show your work.

> SHOW YOUR WORK

4. Nolan is trying to solve 542 × 12 = ___. See his work below. What mistake did he make?

I broke 12 up into 10 and 2.
542 × 10 = 5,420
5,420 × 2 = 10,840

SHOW YOUR WORK

5. Sloane swims 28 laps each day. What is the total number of laps she swims in 2 weeks?

A. 56

B. 232

C. 280

D. 392

SHOW YOUR WORK

6. 50 × 180 = ___ Show your work.

SHOW YOUR WORK

7. The doctor sees 17 patients per day. How many patients does she see in 31 days?

SHOW YOUR WORK

8. 305 × 607 = ___ Show your work.

SHOW YOUR WORK

9. 253 × 15 = ___ Show your work.

SHOW YOUR WORK

10. Gina sold 156 boxes of cookies for her class fundraiser. Each box cost $12. How much money did Gina make?

SHOW YOUR WORK

Dividing Multi-Digit Whole Numbers

We can use what we know about equations, area models and arrays to divide multi-digit whole numbers. Let's look at an example.

Example: **432 ÷ 36 = ___.**

A. 9

B. 10

C. 11

D. 12

There are a couple of different ways to solve this problem. Since it's a multiple choice question, we can use what we know about equations to solve it.

Step 1: Rewrite the equation as multiplication.

We know that 432 ÷ 36 = ___ is the same as ___ × 36 = 432

Step 2: Plug each answer choice into the multiplication problem to see which one gives you **432**.

$9 \times 36 = 324$ ✗ $10 \times 36 = 360$ ✗ $11 \times 36 = 396$ ✗

$12 \times 36 = 432$ ✓

But what if the equation isn't written as a multiple choice problem?
We can use what we know about area models to solve multi-digit division problems that aren't written as multiple choice problems. Let's look at the example again.

Example: **432 ÷ 36 = ___.**

Step 1: Rewrite the equation as multiplication.

We know that 432 ÷ 36 = ___ is the same as ___ × 36 = 432

Step 2: Draw an area model to help you visualize the missing number.

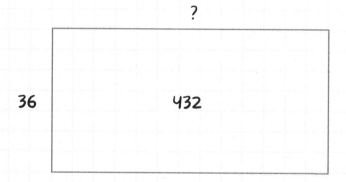

Step 3: Use number sense to break the larger number up into partial products. Start with what you know. We know that **36 × 10 = 360**. So, we will update our model to reflect this knowledge.

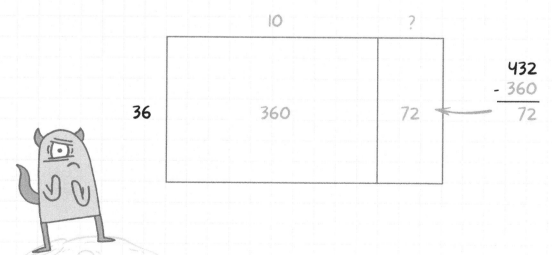

Step 4: Complete the area model.

We need to figure out how many times **36** goes into **72**. I'll use repeated subtraction to see how many times **36** fits into **72**.

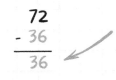

$$\begin{array}{r} 72 \\ - 36 \\ \hline 36 \end{array}$$

I can see that **36** goes into **72** twice.

	10	+	2
36	360		72

Step 5: Fill in the equation.

$$10 + 2 = 12$$

$$12 \times 36 = 432 ✓$$

NOTES

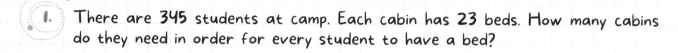

Practice Questions

1. There are **345** students at camp. Each cabin has **23** beds. How many cabins do they need in order for every student to have a bed?

A. 13

B. 14

C. 15

D. 16

SHOW YOUR WORK

2. 288 ÷ 12 = ___ Check your work using multiplication.

SHOW YOUR WORK

3. There are **672** cupcakes at the wedding. Each table has **21** cupcakes. How many tables are at the wedding?

A. 31

B. 32

C. 33

D. 34

SHOW YOUR WORK

4. 1,728 ÷ 48 = ___ Use an area model to solve the equation.

SHOW YOUR WORK

5. 2,214 ÷ 82 = ___ Check your work using multiplication.

SHOW YOUR WORK

6. Tia's car travels **20** miles on each gallon of gas. Her grandma lives **700** miles away. How many gallons of gas does Tia need to get to her grandma's house?

A. 34

B. 35

C. 36

D. 37

SHOW YOUR WORK

7. 1,440 ÷ 12 = ___ Use an area model to solve the equation.

SHOW YOUR WORK

8. 5,096 ÷ 14 = ___ Check your work using multiplication.

SHOW YOUR WORK

9. Zofia is sorting apples at her orchard. She needs to put 64 apples in each basket. She has 1,088 apples in all. How many baskets can she fill?

A. 14

B. 15

C. 16

D. 17

SHOW YOUR WORK

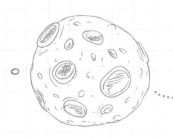

10. 1,243 ÷ 11 = ___ Use an area model to solve the equation.

SHOW YOUR WORK

NOTES

   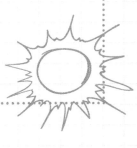

Add, Subtract, Multiply, and Divide Decimals

We can use what we've learned about place value to add, subtract, multiply and divide decimals.

Adding and Subtracting

There are two ways to approach adding and subtracting decimals. The first is to break numbers up based on place value. Let's give that a try.

$$3.5 + 2.5 = \_\_\_$$

Step 1: Break the numbers apart using your knowledge of place value.

3.5 can be broken into 3.0 + 0.5
2.5 can be broken into 2.0 + 0.5

Step 2: Combine digits with the same place value.

3.0 + 2.0 = **5.0**

0.5 + 0.5 = **1.0**

} **5.0 + 1.0 = 6 .0**

3.5 + 2.5 = 6.0

Try it another way

The other way to approach adding and subtracting decimals is to line the numbers up based on place value. Let's try it with subtraction.

$$5.75 - 3.5 = \_\_\_$$

Step 1: Line up the decimal points.

$$\begin{array}{r} 5.75 \\ -\ 3.5 \\ \hline \end{array}$$ ← Notice there's a blank space.

Step 2: Add zeros to make the columns even.

$$5.75$$
$$- \ 3.50$$

You can add a zero to the end of any decimal without changing its value.

Step 3: Subtract as you would whole numbers.

$$5.75$$
$$- \ 3.50$$
$$2.25$$

$$5.75 - 3.5 = 2.25$$

Multiplying

$$6.5 × 2.4 = \_\_\_$$

Step 1: Estimate your answer
Round to the nearest whole number to make an accurate estimate.

$$6.5 × 2.4 = \_\_\_$$
$$\lor \qquad \lor$$
$$7 \ × \ 2 \ = 14$$

My estimate is that the product will be close to 14

Step 2: Multiply as if both factos are whole numbers.

$$6.5 × 2.4 = \_\_\_$$
$$\lor \qquad \lor$$
$$65 × 24 = 1,560$$

Step 3: Add the decimal

This is a very important step. Without the decimal, the answer is incorrect. Look back at the original equation. Count the number of digits behind each decimal point.

$$6.5 \times 2.4 =$$

There is one number after each decimal point, which is a total of two numbers. So, we need to place two digits behind the decimal point in the final product.

Step 4: Check your estimate

Your estimate will help you determine if your decimal is in the correct place.

Estimate: 14   Product: 15.6

15.6 ✓

Dividing

$$8.23 \div 0.2 = \_\_\_$$

Step 1: Rewrite the divisor as a whole number.

$$8.23 \div 0.2 = \_\_\_$$
$$\lor$$
$$2$$

Step 2: Move the decimal in the dividend the same number of spaces. Add zeros if necessary.

$$8.23 \div 0.2 = \_\_\_$$
$$\lor \quad \lor$$
$$82.3 \div 2$$

Step 3: Rewrite the problem. Bring the decimal up to keep track of place value.

$$2 \,|\, \overline{82.3}$$

Step 4: Divide as you would whole numbers.

```
        41.15
  2 |   82.3
    -   8
        2. 3
      - 2
          3
        - 2
         10
       - 10
          0
```

8.23 ÷ 0.2 = 41.15 ✓

NOTES

Practice Questions

 1. 3.5 × 6.3 = ___ Show your work.

SHOW YOUR WORK

2. Katie is baking a cake. The recipe asks for **3.75** cups of milk and **.75** cups of water and **1.25** cups of oil. How much liquid is in the recipe?

SHOW YOUR WORK

3. 9.12 ÷ 0.4 = ___ Show your work.

SHOW YOUR WORK

4. 198.2 - 36.4 = ___ Show your work.

SHOW YOUR WORK

5. Kylie reads 12.5 pages of her book each night. How many pages does she read in 2.5 days?

SHOW YOUR WORK

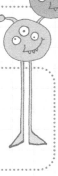

6. 5.67 + .6 + 12.3 =

SHOW YOUR WORK

7. Marvis had $312.75. He purchased a necktie for $17.25. How much money does he have after his purchase?

SHOW YOUR WORK

8. 1.75 ÷ 0.2 = ___ Show your work.

SHOW YOUR WORK

9. Joe has $67.50. He spends $9.75 on a snack after school. How much money does Joe have after buying his snack?

SHOW YOUR WORK

10. 45.90 + 6.50 + 8.7 =

SHOW YOUR WORK

NOTES

1. Sam is buying groceries. The blueberries cost $.25 per pound. How much will 12 pounds of blueberries cost?

SHOW YOUR WORK

2. The value of 8 in 175.879 is ___ times the value of the 8 in 75.789

A. $\frac{1}{10}$

B. 10

C. 100

SHOW YOUR WORK

3. 364 × 14 = ___ Show your work.

SHOW YOUR WORK

4. 3.75×10^2 ___ 8.9×10^1

A. >

B. <

C. =

SHOW YOUR WORK

5. What is another way to write 1.07×10^4?

A. 107

B. 1,070

C. 10,700

SHOW YOUR WORK

6. $518 \div 37 =$ ___ Show your work.

SHOW YOUR WORK

7. Sarah has **$128.90**. She buys **2** dresses for **$26.25** each. How much money does she have after her purchases?

SHOW YOUR WORK

8. Write **10.754** in expanded form.

SHOW YOUR WORK

9. 29.44 ÷ 9.2 = ___ Show your work.

SHOW YOUR WORK

10. Sierra donated **25** packs of erasers to her school. Each pack contained 124 erasers. How many total erasers did Sierra donate to her school?

SHOW YOUR WORK

11. 4 tenths × $\frac{1}{10}$ =

A. 4 hundredths

B. 4 tenths

C. 4 hundreds

D. 4 thousands

SHOW YOUR WORK

12. Julie orders a cheeseburger for **$15.75** and one drink for **$3.50**. She pays with a **$20** bill. How much change will she get?

> SHOW YOUR WORK

13. $5.670 \times 10^2 = $ ___ Show your work

A. .0567

B. 56.70

C. 567.0

D. 5,670

> SHOW YOUR WORK

14. 3.750 ___ 3.75

A. >

B. <

C. =

> SHOW YOUR WORK

15. 6 hundredths × $\frac{1}{10}$ =

A. 6 thousandths

B. 6 tenths

C. 6 tens

D. 6 thousands

SHOW YOUR WORK

16. Which number is not equivalent to 71 when rounded to the nearest whole number?

A. 71.03

B. 71.50

C. 70.90

D. 70.50

SHOW YOUR WORK

17. Round 1.698 to the nearest hundredth

SHOW YOUR WORK

18. Johanna swims 16 laps a day. How many laps does she swim in 21 days?

SHOW YOUR WORK

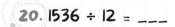

19. ___ < 5.09

A. 5.1

B. 15.99

C. 05.09

D. 5.089

SHOW YOUR WORK

20. 1536 ÷ 12 = ___

SHOW YOUR WORK

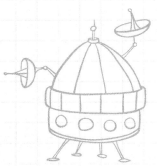

Chapter 3
Number & Operations - Fractions

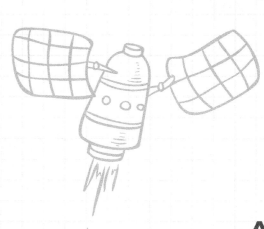

ARGOPREP
STUDY SMARTER, NOT HARDER

Fractions must have a common denominator in order to be added to, or subtracted from, one another. Consider the problem $\frac{1}{3} + \frac{3}{4} = $ ___. We can't add the numbers as they are written. So, how do we proceed?

Step 1: Find a common denominator

We need to rewrite $\frac{1}{3}$ and $\frac{3}{4}$ so that they have the same denominator.

$$\frac{1}{3} + \frac{3}{4} = \text{\_}$$

To find the common denominator, we simply need to determine the least common multiple of **3** and **4**. We can do this using multiplication facts.

3	1	2	3	4
	3	6	9	12

4	1	2	3	4
	4	8	12	16

The least common denominator is 12.

Step 2: Rewrite the equation

We need to rewrite the equation using the common denominator.

We can see in the multiplication chart, that to get 12, we need to multiply 3 by 4.

$$\frac{1}{3} + \frac{3}{4}$$

We can see in the multiplication chart, that to get 12, we need to multiply 4 by 3.

Whatever we do to the bottom number, we have to do to the top number as well. So, we need to muliply 1 by 4.

$$4 \times \frac{1}{3 \times 4} + 3 \times \frac{3}{4 \times 3}$$

Whatever we do to the bottom number, we have to do to the top number as well. So, we need to muliply 3 by 3.

$$\frac{4}{12} + \frac{9}{12}$$

Even though these fractions look different, they express the same value. They are equivalent.

Step 3: Add

Now that we have common denominators, we can add our fractions. Remember, you only add the top numbers.

$$\frac{4}{12} + \frac{9}{12} = \frac{13}{12}$$

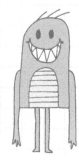

Practice Questions

1. $\frac{1}{3} + \frac{3}{4} =$ ___ Show your work.

SHOW YOUR WORK

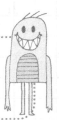

2. $\frac{1}{2} + 2\frac{1}{4} =$ ___ Show your work.

SHOW YOUR WORK

3. $3\frac{5}{6} - \frac{1}{2} =$ ___ Show your work.

SHOW YOUR WORK

4. $\frac{7}{8} + \frac{3}{4} + \frac{1}{16} =$ ___ Show your work.

SHOW YOUR WORK

5. $4\frac{2}{5} - 1\frac{3}{10} = $ _____ Show your work.

SHOW YOUR WORK

6. $7\frac{1}{2} - 3\frac{1}{6} = $ _____ Show your work.

SHOW YOUR WORK

7. $\frac{3}{4} - \frac{1}{12} = $ _____ Show your work.

SHOW YOUR WORK

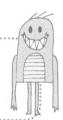

8. $\frac{1}{2} - \frac{3}{7} = $ _____ Show your work.

SHOW YOUR WORK

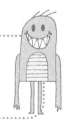

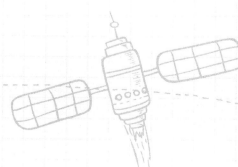

9. $\frac{1}{3} + \frac{4}{9} + \frac{8}{9} =$ ___ Show your work.

SHOW YOUR WORK

10. $\frac{2}{3} + \frac{5}{6} =$ ___ Show your work.

SHOW YOUR WORK

NOTES

Solve Word Problems Involving Addition and Subtraction of Fractions

Sometimes fractions will be presented in word problems. We can use area models and equations to solve these more complicated problems.

Consider the problem below.

Sarah spent $\frac{1}{3}$ of her money on dinner and $\frac{1}{6}$ of her money on dessert.

What fraction of her money did she spend in all?
Draw a model and write an equation to show your work.

Step 1: **Write an equation**

Use what you know to write an equation. We know that this is an addition problem because it is asking how much ribbon was used in all. We can also identify the two parts as $\frac{1}{3}$ and $\frac{1}{6}$.

$$\frac{1}{3} + \frac{1}{6} = \text{---}$$

We need to find a common denominator in order to proceed.

3	$\frac{1}{3}$	$\frac{2}{6}$
6	$\frac{1}{6}$	$\frac{2}{12}$

The common denominator is 6.

$$\frac{2}{6} + \frac{1}{6} = \text{---}$$

Step 2: Draw a model

Use the common denominator to set up your models. Let's use an area model. Since our common denominator is **6**, we need to set each model up with **6** rectangles.

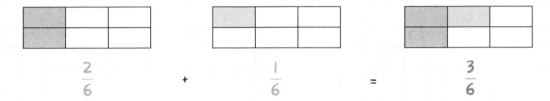

$$\frac{2}{6} \quad + \quad \frac{1}{6} \quad = \quad \frac{3}{6}$$

Step 3: Solve

We can see just by looking at the area model that $\frac{3}{6}$ is equivalent to $\frac{1}{2}$ the area model. When writing your answer, remember to look back at the question. For example, the answer to our problem isn't $\frac{1}{3} + \frac{1}{6} = \frac{1}{2}$. It's Sarah spent $\frac{1}{2}$ her money.

NOTES

Practice Questions

1. Amelia drank $\frac{1}{3}$ of her water bottle before swim practice. She drank another $\frac{1}{6}$ of her water bottle after practice. What fraction of water did she drink from her water bottle? Draw a model and write an equation to show your work.

SHOW YOUR WORK

2. David needs to walk his dog $\frac{3}{4}$ of a mile. He already walked him $\frac{1}{2}$ mile. How much farther does he need to walk? Which expression represents the word problem?

A. $\frac{1}{2} - \frac{3}{4}$

B. $\frac{1}{2} + \frac{3}{4}$

C. $\frac{3}{4} - \frac{1}{2}$

D. $\frac{3}{4} + \frac{1}{2}$

SHOW YOUR WORK

3. Sarah has $5\frac{1}{6}$ yards of ribbon. She cuts $1\frac{1}{6}$ yards off for a friend. How much ribbon does she have left? Draw a model and write an equation to show your work.

SHOW YOUR WORK

4. Jim is making punch. He mixes $\frac{1}{5}$ cup of orange juice with $\frac{2}{3}$ cups of apple juice. How much juice is does he use in all? Which expression represents the word problem?

A. $\frac{1}{5} + \frac{2}{3}$

B. $\frac{2}{3} - \frac{1}{5}$

C. $\frac{1}{5} \times \frac{2}{3}$

D. $\frac{1}{5} \div \frac{2}{3}$

SHOW YOUR WORK

5. Kira walked $3\frac{2}{3}$ miles yesterday. She walked another $4\frac{5}{6}$ miles today. How many miles did she walk yesterday and today combined? Draw a model and write an equation to show your work.

SHOW YOUR WORK

6. Which equation is incorrect?

A. $\frac{3}{4} - \frac{1}{4} = \frac{1}{2}$

B. $\frac{1}{2} - \frac{1}{4} = \frac{3}{4}$

C. $\frac{1}{4} + \frac{1}{2} = \frac{3}{4}$

SHOW YOUR WORK

7. Carlos and Rachel are peeling apples for a pie. Carlos peels $\frac{2}{5}$ of the apples. Rachel peels $\frac{1}{4}$ of the apples what fraction of the apples have they peeled so far? Draw a model and write an equation to show your work.

SHOW YOUR WORK

8. Matt is required to read $2\frac{1}{2}$ hours for homework each day. He has already completed $1\frac{3}{5}$ hours of today's reading. How much longer does he need to read today? Draw a model and write an equation to show your work.

SHOW YOUR WORK

9. Eliza has $6\frac{5}{6}$ cups of flour. She used $2\frac{1}{2}$ cups to bake a pie. How many cups of flour does Eliza have left? Draw a model and write an equation to show your work.

SHOW YOUR WORK

10. $\frac{3}{4} + \frac{1}{8} = \frac{1}{2}$

SHOW YOUR WORK

A. True

B. False

11. George drove $6\frac{9}{10}$ hours on Saturday. He drove $5\frac{1}{2}$ hours on Sunday. How many hours did George drive in all? Draw a model and write an equation to show your work.

SHOW YOUR WORK

12. Anna is sewing a costume. She needs $\frac{5}{6}$ yards of blue fabric and $\frac{3}{4}$ yards of green fabric. How many yards of fabric does she need to make her costume?

A. $\frac{1}{8}$ yards

SHOW YOUR WORK

B. $\frac{1}{2}$ yards

C. $1\frac{7}{12}$ yards

13. Sandy is making a sandwich. She uses $\frac{1}{8}$ pounds of turkey and $\frac{1}{16}$ pounds of salami. She also uses $\frac{1}{4}$ pounds of ham. How many pounds of meat does she use on her sandwich? Draw a model and write an equation to show your work.

SHOW YOUR WORK

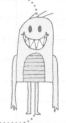

14. Leonardo used $\frac{3}{4}$ ounces of milk to make a cake. He has $3\frac{1}{2}$ ounces of milk left. How much milk did he have before making his cake?

SHOW YOUR WORK

15. Zoey used $\frac{2}{3}$ yards of yarn to knit a hat. She now has $12\frac{1}{6}$ yards. How much yarn did she have before she knit the hat? Draw a model and write an equation to show your work.

SHOW YOUR WORK

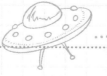

16. Kate spends $\frac{3}{5}$ of her money on a new dress and $\frac{1}{15}$ of her money on new socks.

How much of her money did she spend in all?

SHOW YOUR WORK

17. Albert has $5\frac{1}{2}$ gallons of glue. He uses $3\frac{1}{4}$ gallons to make slime with his class.

How many gallons of glue does he have left?

SHOW YOUR WORK

18. Jacob's hair is $3\frac{1}{3}$ feet long. He cuts $\frac{1}{6}$ feet of his hair off. How much hair does he have left?

SHOW YOUR WORK

19. Alex read $\frac{1}{3}$ of his book on Tuesday and $\frac{1}{9}$ of his book on Wednesday. How

much of his book has he read so far?

SHOW YOUR WORK

20. Baylee's math class is $1\frac{1}{2}$ hours long. She has been in class for $\frac{3}{4}$ an hour so

far. How much time is left in the class?

SHOW YOUR WORK

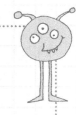

NOTES

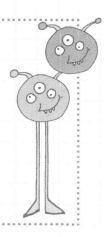

A fraction is a division problem. The numerator represents the dividend (the number that is being divided). The denominator represents the divisor (the number the dividend is divided by). So, the fraction a/b is equivalent to the equation a ÷ b.

For example: $1 \div 2 = \dfrac{1}{2}$

I whole

I whole divided into **2** parts

Consider the word problem below.

3 people want to share 4 candy bars. If the candy bars are shared evenly, how much candy will each person get?

Step 1: Determine what you know

We know that 4 candy bars can't be shared as wholes amongst 3 people. The candy bars will need to be cut up into fractions.

Step 2: Draw a model

We will start by drawing the 4 candy bars.

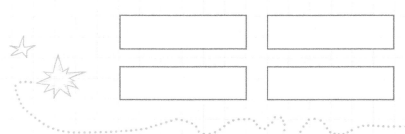

Since there are three people, we will cut each candy bar into thirds.

$\frac{1}{3}$	$\frac{1}{3}$	$\frac{1}{3}$

$\frac{1}{3}$	$\frac{1}{3}$	$\frac{1}{3}$

$\frac{1}{3}$	$\frac{1}{3}$	$\frac{1}{3}$

$\frac{1}{3}$	$\frac{1}{3}$	$\frac{1}{3}$

Step 3: Divide

We need to use the model to divide (or hand out) the pieces among the three people. We can label, or color, each piece to help us keep track of how many pieces each person receives.

$\frac{1}{3}$	$\frac{1}{3}$	$\frac{1}{3}$

$\frac{1}{3}$	$\frac{1}{3}$	$\frac{1}{3}$

$\frac{1}{3}$	$\frac{1}{3}$	$\frac{1}{3}$

$\frac{1}{3}$	$\frac{1}{3}$	$\frac{1}{3}$

Blue - Person 1   Green - Person 2   Purple - Person 3

Step 4: Solve

We can see that each person gets four $\frac{1}{3}$ pieces of candy bar

$$\frac{1}{3} + \frac{1}{3} + \frac{1}{3} + \frac{1}{3} = \frac{4}{3}$$

Each person will receive $\frac{4}{3}$ candy bars.

ARGOPREP

Practice Questions

1. There are 4 people at the party but only 3 cupcakes. Draw a picture to show how the cupcakes could be shared?

SHOW YOUR WORK

2. 5 people want to share 3 pizzas. How much pizza will each person get?

A. $\frac{2}{3}$

B. $\frac{3}{5}$

C. $1\frac{2}{3}$

D. $2\frac{2}{3}$

SHOW YOUR WORK

3. Nina has 7 cookies. Her mom tells her to split them evenly between herself and her brother. How many cookies do they each get? Draw a picture to show the division.

SHOW YOUR WORK

4. 8 field hockey players need to split **78** ounces of water. If the coach splits the water evenly, how much water will each player get?

A. 9 ounces

B. $9\frac{3}{4}$ ounces

C. 10 ounces

D. $10\frac{1}{2}$ ounces

SHOW YOUR WORK

5. Louis has **36** ounces of juice. He puts the juice in **4** jugs. How many ounces of juice is in each jug? Draw a picture to show the division.

SHOW YOUR WORK

6. Sarah made **12** cookies for her sleepover. If she splits the cookies evenly between her **5** friends, how many cookies will each friend get?

A. $1\frac{2}{5}$

B. $1\frac{3}{4}$

C. $2\frac{2}{5}$

D. $3\frac{3}{4}$

SHOW YOUR WORK

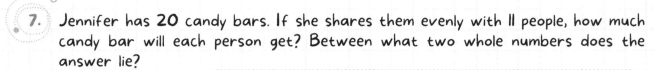

7. Jennifer has **20** candy bars. If she shares them evenly with **11** people, how much candy bar will each person get? Between what two whole numbers does the answer lie?

A. 1 and 2

B. 2 and 3

C. 3 and 4

SHOW YOUR WORK

8. Harold has **20** ounces of punch. If he shares the punch evenly between his **6** friends, how many ounces of punch could each friend have? Between what two whole numbers does the answer lie?

A. 1 and 2

B. 2 and 3

C. 3 and 4

SHOW YOUR WORK

9. Daneel wants to get rid of his Halloween candy. If he splits **5** bags of candy evenly between **4** friends, how many bags of candy will each friend get? Between what two whole numbers does the answer lie?

A. 1 and 2

B. 2 and 3

C. 3 and 4

SHOW YOUR WORK

10. Sandra brings **22** ounces of slime to school. If she splits all of the slime evenly with her **9** classmates, how many ounces of slime will each student get? Between what two whole numbers does the answer lie?

A. 1 and 2

B. 2 and 3

C. 3 and 4

SHOW YOUR WORK

NOTES

Multiplying with Fractions

In a way, multiplying fractions is quicker than adding fractions. There's no need to find a common denominator. Consider the problem below.

$$\frac{1}{2} \times \frac{3}{4} =$$

Step 1: Multiply the two numerators

$$\frac{1}{2} \times \frac{3}{4} = \frac{3}{?}$$

Step 2: Multiply the two denominators

$$\frac{1}{2} \times \frac{3}{4} = \frac{3}{8}$$

Step 3: Simplify

When dealing with larger numbers, you'll need to simplify your answer. In this case, the fraction $\frac{3}{8}$ is already simplified.

What if I want to find the area of a rectangle?

You can use an area model to find the area of a rectangle with fractional lengths. Consider the problem below.

Find the area of a rectangle with a length of $4\frac{1}{2}$ units and a width **5** units.

Step 1: **Draw the area model**

We know that area = length x width. We will use these units to set-up our model

5

1	1	1	1	1
1	1	1	1	1
1	1	1	1	1
1	1	1	1	1
$\frac{1}{2}$	$\frac{1}{2}$	$\frac{1}{2}$	$\frac{1}{2}$	$\frac{1}{2}$

$4\frac{1}{2}$ (to the left of the grid)

Step 2: Multiply

$$5 \times 4\frac{1}{2} =$$
$$\vee$$
$$\frac{5}{1} \times \frac{9}{2} = \frac{45}{2}$$
$$\vee$$
$$22\frac{1}{2}$$

Step 3: Check your work

You can check your multiplication by adding the units in your area model.

1	1	1	1	1
1	1	1	1	1
1	1	1	1	1
1	1	1	1	1
$\frac{1}{2}$	$\frac{1}{2}$	$\frac{1}{2}$	$\frac{1}{2}$	$\frac{1}{2}$

$$4\frac{1}{2} + 4\frac{1}{2} + 4\frac{1}{2} + 4\frac{1}{2} + 4\frac{1}{2} = 22\frac{1}{2}$$

NOTES

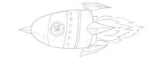

Practice Questions

1. $5 \times \frac{1}{4} =$ ___

SHOW YOUR WORK

2. $\frac{2}{3} \times 9 =$ ___

SHOW YOUR WORK

3. $7 \times \frac{5}{12} =$ ___

SHOW YOUR WORK

4. $9 \times \frac{1}{2} =$ ___

SHOW YOUR WORK

5. $3 \times \dfrac{3}{4} = $ ___

SHOW YOUR WORK

6. $6 \times \dfrac{2}{3} = $ ___

SHOW YOUR WORK

7. $2 \times \dfrac{5}{6} = $ ___

SHOW YOUR WORK

8. $4 \times \dfrac{3}{4} = $ ___

SHOW YOUR WORK

9. $3 \times \dfrac{2}{5} =$ ___

SHOW YOUR WORK

10. $\dfrac{1}{2} \times 7 =$ ___

SHOW YOUR WORK

Use the rectangle below to answer questions 11 - 13.

1	1	$\dfrac{1}{2}$
1	1	$\dfrac{1}{2}$

11. The rectangle is ___ units long.

A. 1

B. 2

C. $2\dfrac{1}{2}$

SHOW YOUR WORK

12. The rectangle is ___ units wide.

A. 1

B. 2

C. $2\frac{1}{2}$

SHOW YOUR WORK

13. The area of the rectangle is ___ units²

A. $2\frac{1}{2}$

B. $4\frac{1}{2}$

C. 5

SHOW YOUR WORK

Use the rectangle below to answer questions 14 - 16.

1	1
1	1
1	1
$\frac{1}{2}$	$\frac{1}{2}$

14. The rectangle is ___ units long.

A. 1

B. 2

C. $3\frac{1}{2}$

SHOW YOUR WORK

15. The rectangle is ___ units wide.

A. 1

B. 2

C. $3\frac{1}{2}$

SHOW YOUR WORK

16. The area of the rectangle is ___ units^2

A. $3\frac{1}{2}$

B. $6\frac{1}{2}$

C. 7

SHOW YOUR WORK

17. Find the area of a rectangle with a length of $2\frac{1}{2}$ units and a width of **5** units.

SHOW YOUR WORK

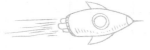

18. Find the area of a rectangle with a length of $4\frac{1}{2}$ and a width of 4.

SHOW YOUR WORK

19. Find the area of a rectangle with a length of 7 units and a width of $6\frac{1}{2}$ units.

SHOW YOUR WORK

20. Find the area of a rectangle with a length of $2\frac{1}{3}$ and a width of 2 units.

SHOW YOUR WORK

Multiplying to Scale

Numbers can be scaled using multiplication. Consider the model below.

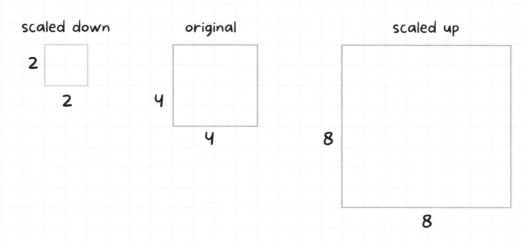

scaled down

2

2

original

4

4

scaled up

8

8

Scaling Up

Multiplying a number by a fraction greater than 1 results in a product greater than the original number. Our model was scaled up by a factor of two, $4 \times 2 = 8$.

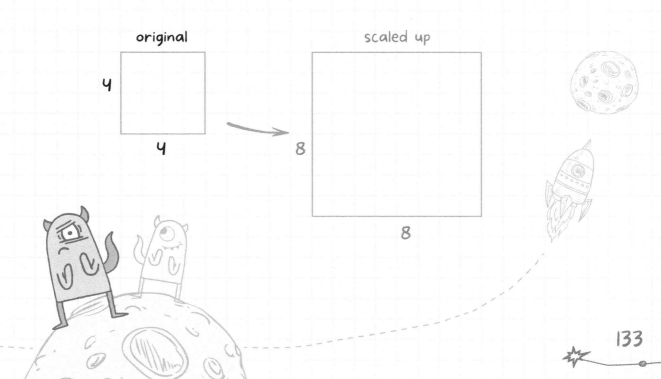

original

4

4

scaled up

8

8

Scaling Down

Multiplying a number by a fraction less than I results in a product smaller than the original number. Remember that multiplying a number by a fraction less than one is the same as dividing by a number greater than 1.

Our model was scaled down by one-half, $4 \times \dfrac{1}{2} = 2$ or $\dfrac{4}{2} = 2$

scaled down

2 ☐
2

original

4 ☐
4

What if we multiply a number by a fraction equal to I?

Multiplying a number by a fraction equal to I results in a product equal to the original number

NOTES

Practice Questions

1. When multiplied by **2**, is $\frac{1}{2}$ scaled up or down? Explain your answer.

SHOW YOUR WORK

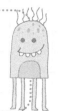

2. When multiplied by $\frac{1}{2}$, is **2** scaled up or down? Explain your answer.

SHOW YOUR WORK

3. Which expression is greater than $\frac{8}{9}$? Select your answer without multiplying.

A. $\frac{8}{9} \times \frac{3}{3}$

B. $\frac{8}{9} \times \frac{1}{4}$

C. $\frac{8}{9} \times \frac{3}{2}$

SHOW YOUR WORK

4. $5 \times \dfrac{3}{3}$ ___ 5. Explain your answer.

   A. <

   B. >

   C. =

SHOW YOUR WORK

5. Which expression is less than $\dfrac{3}{5}$. Select your answer without multiplying.

   A. $\dfrac{3}{5} \times \dfrac{2}{2}$

   B. $\dfrac{3}{5} \times \dfrac{7}{8}$

   C. $\dfrac{3}{5} \times \dfrac{2}{1}$

SHOW YOUR WORK

6. When multiplied by $\dfrac{8}{2}$ is 2 scaled up or down? Explain your answer.

SHOW YOUR WORK

7. $8 \times \dfrac{3}{5}$ ___ 8. Explain your answer.

   A. <

   B. >

   C. =

SHOW YOUR WORK

8. Which expression is less than $4\frac{7}{8}$? Select your answer without multiplying.

A. $4\frac{7}{8} \times 1$

B. $4\frac{7}{8} \times \frac{2}{1}$

C. $4\frac{7}{8} \times \frac{3}{4}$

SHOW YOUR WORK

9. When multiplied by $\frac{1}{4}$ is 17 scaled up or down? Explain your answer.

SHOW YOUR WORK

10. Which expression is greater than $6\frac{3}{4}$? Select your answer without multiplying.

A. $6\frac{3}{4} \times \frac{2}{9}$

B. $6\frac{3}{4} \times \frac{9}{9}$

C. $6\frac{3}{4} \times \frac{3}{2}$

SHOW YOUR WORK

11. When multiplied by $\frac{9}{7}$ is 3 scaled up or down? Explain your answer.

SHOW YOUR WORK

12. Which expression is greater than $\frac{2}{3}$? Select your answer without multiplying.

A. $\frac{2}{3} \times \frac{3}{4}$

B. $\frac{2}{3} \times \frac{8}{8}$

C. $\frac{2}{3} \times \frac{12}{9}$

SHOW YOUR WORK

13. When multiplied by ___ is **65** scaled down. Explain your answer

A. $\frac{6}{5}$

B. $\frac{5}{5}$

C. $\frac{5}{6}$

SHOW YOUR WORK

14. $5 \times \frac{5}{8}$ ___ 5. Explain your answer.

A. $<$

B. $>$

C. $=$

SHOW YOUR WORK

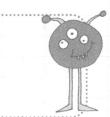

15. Which expression is greater than $\frac{8}{9}$? Select your answer without multiplying.

A. $\frac{8}{9} \times 1$

B. $\frac{8}{9} \times \frac{10}{12}$

C. $\frac{8}{9} \times \frac{2}{1}$

SHOW YOUR WORK

16. $2\frac{1}{2} \times \frac{7}{7}$ ___ $2\frac{1}{2}$. Explain your answer.

A. <

B. >

C. =

SHOW YOUR WORK

17. Which expression is equal to 64? Select your answer without multiplying.

A. $64 \times \frac{1}{64}$

B. $64 \times \frac{64}{1}$

C. $64 \times \frac{64}{64}$

SHOW YOUR WORK

18. Which expression is less than 4? Select your answer without multiplying.

A. $4 \times \frac{5}{4}$

B. $4 \times \frac{3}{3}$

C. $4 \times \frac{1}{2}$

SHOW YOUR WORK

19. When multiplied by ___ is 81 scaled up. Explain your answer

A. $\frac{1}{8}$

B. $\frac{8}{8}$

C. $\frac{9}{8}$

SHOW YOUR WORK

20. $5 \times \dfrac{1}{2}$ ___ 5. Select your answer without multiplying.

A. >

B. <

C. =

SHOW YOUR WORK

NOTES

Solve Real World Problems Involving Multiplication of Fractions

There are times when we need to multiply fractions in the real world. Consider the problem below.

Janey runs $\frac{1}{2}$ mile. Sarah runs $\frac{3}{4}$ of the distance Janey runs. How far does Sarah run?

Step 1: **Write the equation**

Janey runs $\frac{1}{2}$. Sarah runs $\frac{3}{4}$ that distance. So, we want to find $\frac{3}{4}$ of $\frac{1}{2}$. The word **of** tells us that this is a multiplication problem.

$$\frac{3}{4} \times \frac{1}{2} = \text{\_\_\_}$$

We know that the answer will be less than $\frac{3}{4}$ because we are multiplying by a fraction smaller than 1. We also know that we can multiply across to find the product.

$$\frac{3}{4} \times \frac{1}{2} = \frac{3}{8}$$

Let's use a model to check our answer.

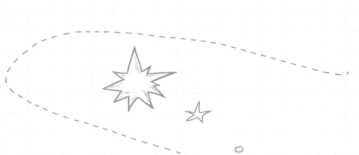

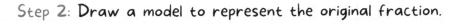

Step 2: Draw a model to represent the original fraction.

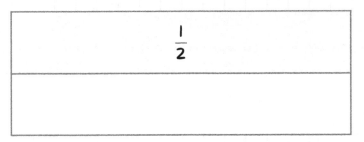

$\dfrac{1}{2}$

Step 3: Divide the first model to represent the second fraction

Use the denominator to determine how many pieces you need to divide the model. Since the denominator is 4, we will draw four vertical lines.

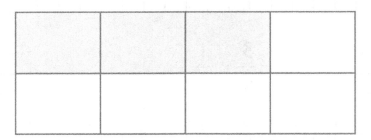

Step 4: Solve

We can see that the model represents $\dfrac{3}{8}$ units. So, Sara runs $\dfrac{3}{8}$ miles. Our answer from step 1 is correct.

Practice Questions

1. Frank jumps $3\frac{3}{4}$ feet. Brittany jumps $\frac{1}{8}$ the distance Frank jumps. How far did

Brittany jump? Write and equation and draw a model to show your thinking.

SHOW YOUR WORK

2. John lives 7 miles from work. The train takes him $\frac{2}{3}$ of the way to work. How

many miles does John ride the train? Write and equation and draw a model to
show your thinking.

SHOW YOUR WORK

3. Stephanie has a $\frac{1}{2}$ pound of chocolate. She ate $\frac{3}{4}$ of it. How many pounds of

chocolate did she eat? Write and equation and draw a model to show your thinking.

SHOW YOUR WORK

4. Raven has **32** ounces of water in her bucket. She uses $\frac{5}{6}$ of the water in her garden. How many ounces of water did she use? Write and equation and draw a model to show your thinking.

SHOW YOUR WORK

5. Jasmine is **6** $\frac{2}{3}$ feet tall. Heather is $\frac{4}{5}$ her height. How many feet tall is Heather?

SHOW YOUR WORK

6. Ben is running a race. He needs to run **6** $\frac{1}{5}$ miles. He's already run $\frac{1}{4}$ of the race. How many miles has he run?

SHOW YOUR WORK

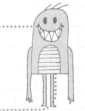

7. Carl studied for **2** $\frac{1}{2}$ hours. During that time, he spent $\frac{1}{3}$ of his time studying science. How many hours did he study science?

SHOW YOUR WORK

8. Sara brought 12 boxes of cupcakes to class. $\frac{1}{4}$ of the cupcakes were vanilla. How many boxes contained vanilla cupcakes?

SHOW YOUR WORK

9. Sierra spent $5\frac{1}{2}$ hours at the zoo. She spent $\frac{1}{3}$ of her time at the gorilla exhibit.

How many hours did she spend at the gorilla exhibit?

SHOW YOUR WORK

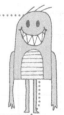

10. Lauren needs to read 13 of the chapters in her book before tomorrow's class. She's already read $\frac{1}{8}$ of the chapters. How many chapters has she read?

SHOW YOUR WORK

145

We can use our knowledge of fractions to solve more complex division problems. Consider the problem below.

Baylee is making sandwiches. Each sandwich takes $\frac{1}{2}$ pound of ham. If Baylee has 5 pounds of ham, how many sandwiches can she make?

Step 1: **Write an equation**

Baylee needs to divide the 5 lbs of ham into $\frac{1}{2}$ pound units. This can be expressed as:

$$5 \div \frac{1}{2} = \text{\_\_\_}$$

Step 2: **Draw a model**

It's important to draw a model to ensure you set your equation up properly. Start by drawing the dividend (the number that will be divided). For this example, we need to draw 5lbs of ham.

1		1	
1		1	

1

Next, we need to divide each pound into $\frac{1}{2}$ pound units.

| $\frac{1}{2}$ | $\frac{1}{2}$ | $\frac{1}{2}$ | $\frac{1}{2}$ | $\frac{1}{2}$ | $\frac{1}{2}$ |
| $\frac{1}{2}$ | $\frac{1}{2}$ | $\frac{1}{2}$ | $\frac{1}{2}$ |

Step 3: Solve

Calculate the number of $\frac{1}{2}$ to determine the number of sandwiches Baylee can make.

$\frac{1}{2}$	$\frac{1}{2}$

$\frac{1}{2}$	$\frac{1}{2}$

$\frac{1}{2}$	$\frac{1}{2}$

$\frac{1}{2}$	$\frac{1}{2}$

$\frac{1}{2}$	$\frac{1}{2}$

$$2 + 2 + 2 + 2 + 2 = 10$$

Step 4: Check your work

You can use multiplication and scaling to check your answer.

$$10 \times \frac{1}{2} = 5 \quad \checkmark$$

$$10 > 5 \quad \checkmark$$

Baylee can make 10 sandwiches

NOTES

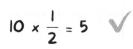

Practice Questions

1. $\frac{1}{2} \div 6 =$ ___ Draw a model to support your answer.

A. $\frac{1}{12}$

B. 12

SHOW YOUR WORK

2. $6 \div \frac{1}{2} =$ ___ Draw a model to support your answer.

A. $\frac{1}{12}$

B. 12

SHOW YOUR WORK

3. $\frac{3}{4} \div 3 =$ ___ Draw a model to support your answer.

A. 4

B. $\frac{1}{4}$

SHOW YOUR WORK

4. $3 \div \frac{3}{4} =$ ___ Draw a model to support your answer.

A. 4

B. $\frac{1}{4}$

SHOW YOUR WORK

5. $\frac{7}{8} \div 7 =$ ___ Draw a model to support your answer.

A. $\frac{1}{8}$

SHOW YOUR WORK

B. 8

6. $7 \div \frac{7}{8} =$ ___ Draw a model to support your answer.

A. $\frac{1}{8}$

SHOW YOUR WORK

B. 8

7. $\frac{5}{9} \div 5 =$ ___ Draw a model to support your answer.

A. $\frac{1}{9}$

SHOW YOUR WORK

B. 9

8. $5 \div \frac{5}{9} =$ ___ Draw a model to support your answer.

A. $\frac{1}{9}$

SHOW YOUR WORK

B. 9

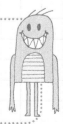

9. $2 \div \dfrac{3}{5} =$ ___ Draw a model to support your answer.

A. $\dfrac{3}{10}$

B. $3\dfrac{1}{3}$

SHOW YOUR WORK

10. $\dfrac{3}{5} \div 2 =$ ___ Draw a model to support your answer.

A. $\dfrac{3}{10}$

B. $3\dfrac{1}{3}$

SHOW YOUR WORK

11. How much water will each person get if 7 people share $12\dfrac{1}{2}$ ounces of water equally? Draw a model to check your answer.

SHOW YOUR WORK

12. How many $\frac{1}{2}$-cup servings are in **6** cups of sugar? Draw a model to check your answer.

SHOW YOUR WORK

13. How much water will each person get if **4** people share **24** $\frac{3}{4}$ ounces of water equally? Draw a model to check your answer.

SHOW YOUR WORK

14. **5** people want to share **2** $\frac{1}{8}$ gallons of ice cream. How much ice cream will each person get? Draw a model to check your answer.

SHOW YOUR WORK

15. Waldo is making mashed potatoes. He has $5\frac{1}{4}$ cups of butter. How many bowls

of mashed potatoes can he make if each bowl needs 2 cups of butter? Draw a model to check your answer.

SHOW YOUR WORK

16. How many $\frac{1}{4}$-cup servings are in 9 cups of milk? Draw a model to check your answer.

SHOW YOUR WORK

17. How much pudding will each kid get if 4 kids share 6 cups of pudding equally? Draw a model to check your answer.

SHOW YOUR WORK

18. Kara is washing cars. She has $32\frac{1}{2}$ gallons of water. How many cars can she wash if each car needs 4 gallons of water? Draw a model to check your answer.

SHOW YOUR WORK

19. Summer is making pie. She has $15\frac{3}{4}$ apples. How many apples will go in each pie if she makes 3 pies. Draw a model to check your answer.

SHOW YOUR WORK

20. How many $\frac{1}{6}$-cup servings are in 3 cups of sugar? Draw a model to check your answer.

SHOW YOUR WORK

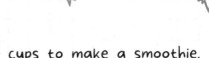

1. Josephina has $3\frac{1}{2}$ cups of blueberries. She used $\frac{3}{4}$ cups to make a smoothie. How many cups of blueberries does Eliza have left?

   SHOW YOUR WORK

2. 6 people want to share 10 pies. How much pie will each person get?

   SHOW YOUR WORK

3. When multiplied by $\frac{1}{2}$ is 4 scaled up or down? Explain your answer.

   SHOW YOUR WORK

4. Which number is less than 19? How can you tell without multiplying?

   A. $19 \times \frac{1}{2}$

   B. $19 \times \frac{2}{2}$

   C. $19 \times \frac{2}{1}$

   SHOW YOUR WORK

5. Sloane is making punch. Each serving takes $\frac{3}{4}$ ounces of apple juice. If Sloane has 5 ounces of juice, how many servings of punch can she make? Use a model to represent the equation.

SHOW YOUR WORK

6. Leo runs 3 miles. Sarah runs $\frac{2}{5}$ of the distance Leo runs. How far does Sarah run?

SHOW YOUR WORK

7. $8 \times \frac{1}{4} = \_\_\_$

SHOW YOUR WORK

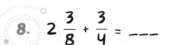

8. $2 \frac{3}{8} + \frac{3}{4} = \text{---}$

SHOW YOUR WORK

9. Sofie is making sandwiches. Each sandwich takes $\frac{3}{4}$ pound of cheese. If Sofie has 4 pounds of cheese, how many sandwiches can she make?

SHOW YOUR WORK

10. $15 \times \frac{3}{4} \text{---} 15.$ How can you tell without multiplying?

A. >

B. <

C. =

SHOW YOUR WORK

11. Brandon is driving to his cousin's house. He drives $5\frac{5}{6}$ hours the first day. He drives another $3\frac{3}{4}$ hours the next day. How many hours did he drive in all?

SHOW YOUR WORK

12. Evan has $3\frac{1}{2}$ pies. He wants to share the pies evenly with his 12 friends. How much pie will each friend get?

SHOW YOUR WORK

13. Mark jumps 8 feet. Sarah jumps $\frac{7}{8}$ of the distance Mark jumps. How far does Sarah jump?

SHOW YOUR WORK

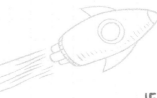

14. $3\frac{1}{2} - 1\frac{1}{9} = $ ___

SHOW YOUR WORK

15. $\frac{9}{2} \times \frac{3}{4} = $ ___

SHOW YOUR WORK

16. Georgia has 13 cookies. If she shares them evenly with 5 people, what fraction of cookies will each person get? Between what two whole numbers does the answer lie?

A. 1 and 2

B. 2 and 3

C. 3 and 4

SHOW YOUR WORK

17. Joanne is making pancakes. She needs $2\frac{3}{4}$ cup of milk. She has $\frac{1}{8}$ cup of milk. How much more milk does she need if she wants to make pancakes?

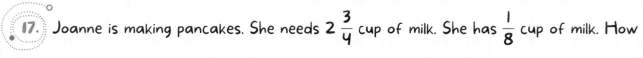

SHOW YOUR WORK

Use the model below to answer questions 18 - 20.

1	1	1	$\frac{3}{4}$
1	1	1	$\frac{3}{4}$
1	1	1	$\frac{3}{4}$
1	1	1	$\frac{3}{4}$

18. The rectangle is ___ units long.

A. 1

B. $3\frac{3}{4}$

C. 4

SHOW YOUR WORK

19. The rectangle is ___ units wide.

A. 1

B. $3\frac{3}{4}$

C. 4

SHOW YOUR WORK

20. The area of the rectangle is ___ units²

A. 14

B. $14\frac{3}{4}$

C. 15

SHOW YOUR WORK

Chapter 4
Measurement & Data

ARGOPREP
STUDY SMARTER, NOT HARDER

We can use what we know about multiplication to convert measurements. Look at the example below.

The average elephant weighs 14,00 pounds. Sarah needs to record the weight in tons for her science project. Use the conversion chart to help her convert pounds to tons.

Step 1: **Write an equation**

This will help you keep track of what you know and what you need to know.

14,000 tons = _____ pounds

Conversion Chart
1 kilogram = 1,000 grams
1 ton = 2,000 pounds
1 pound = 16 ounces

Step 2: **Use the conversion chart**

Identify both units on the conversion chart. For this example, we need to find out how to convert tons to pounds. According to the chart, 1 ton is equivalent to **2,000** pounds.

1 ton = 2,000 pounds   14,000 tons = _____ pounds

Step 3: **Calculate**

Once you know how the units convert, you can calculate the answer. Since every 1 ton has **2,000** pounds. So, we need to multiply 14,000 by **2,000**.

14,000 × 2,000 = _____

Step 4: **Check your answer**

We know that our answer should be larger than the original number since there are **2,000** pounds in 1 ton, and we have 14 tons. We also know that our answer should be labeled in pounds not tons.

✓   ✓

The elephant weighs **28,000,000 pounds**

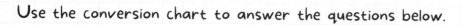
Practice Questions

Use the conversion chart to answer the questions below.

Conversion Chart			
Volume	Length	Weight	Time
1 gallon = 128 fluid ounces	1 kilometer = 1000 meters	1 kilogram = 1000 grams	1 year = 52 weeks
1 pint = 2 cups	1 mile = 5280 feet	1 ton = 2,000 pounds	1 week = 7 days
1 cup = 8 fluid ounces	1 yard = 3 feet	1 pound = 16 ounces	1 minute = 60 seconds

1. Fred brought 16 cups of water to the basketball game. The team drank 46 ounces of water during the game. How many ounces of water did Fred have left after the game?

> SHOW YOUR WORK

2. Hank has to read for 45 minutes each night. How many seconds does Hank have to read each night?

> SHOW YOUR WORK

3. Convert 8 pounds to ounces

SHOW YOUR WORK

4. Alyssa is running a 3-mile race. She already ran $\frac{1}{4}$ of the race. How many feet has she run?

A. $\frac{3}{4}$

B. 34

C. 390

D. 3,960

SHOW YOUR WORK

5. How many weeks are in 3 years?

SHOW YOUR WORK

6. Benjamin weighs 123 pounds. Benjamin's little brother is $\frac{1}{2}$ his weight. How many ounces does Benjamin's brother weigh?

SHOW YOUR WORK

7. Carol has 3 yards of fabric. She shares her fabric evenly with 4 friends. How many feet of fabric does Carol give each friend?

SHOW YOUR WORK

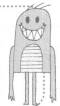

8. Convert 6 cups into pints.

SHOW YOUR WORK

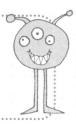

9. Danielle bikes 12 kilometers. Her friend bikes 16 kilometers. How many more meters does Danielle's friend bike?

A. 4

B. 40

C. 400

D. 4,000

SHOW YOUR WORK

10. How many tons is **6,000** pounds?

SHOW YOUR WORK

NOTES

In fourth grade, we used line plots to solve word problems. Line plots can also be used to solve more complex problems. Let's look at an example.

The line plot below represents the amount of time Carla spent studying on **5** different days.

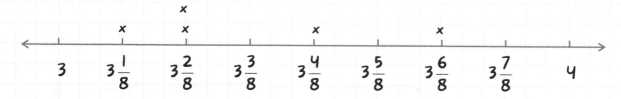

If the total amount of time Carla spent studying was redistributed equally among each of the **5** days, how many hours would Carla study each day?

Step 1: **Collect the data points**

Write down all of the data plots. Remember to write each fraction down the number of times an x appears above it. For this example, we should have **5** total fractions because we have **5** data points (represented as x's on the line plot). We can see that $3\frac{2}{8}$ will be recorded twice.

$$3\frac{1}{8}, \ 3\frac{2}{8}, \ 3\frac{2}{8}, \ 3\frac{4}{8}, \ 3\frac{6}{8}$$

Step 2: **Determine the Operation**

This is a two-step problem. First, we need to add all of the data points together. Then, we need to divide the points across each day.

Step 3: Solve

$$3\frac{1}{8} + 3\frac{2}{8} + 3\frac{2}{8} + 3\frac{4}{8} + 3\frac{6}{8} = 16\frac{7}{8}$$

We can easily add the fractions because they already have the same denominator.

$$16\frac{7}{8} \div 5 = 3\frac{3}{8}$$

Step 4: Check your answer

You can look back at the line plot to make sure your answer looks correct. We can see that $3\frac{3}{8}$ falls reasonoably on the line plot, which means our answer is correct. If we had accidently used the wrong operation in step 2, the answer would look wrong on the line plot.

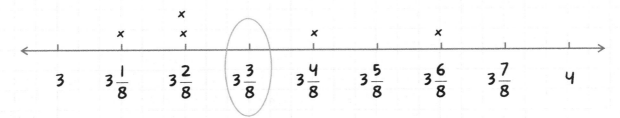

NOTES

ARGOPREP

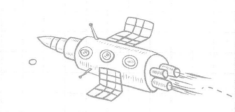

Practice Questions

1. Draw a line plot for the data set below.

$$\frac{1}{4}, \frac{1}{8}, \frac{3}{8}, \frac{3}{4}, \frac{1}{2}, \frac{1}{4}, \frac{9}{12}$$

SHOW YOUR WORK

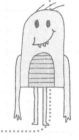

2. Which set of data is represented on the line plot?

A. $\frac{1}{2}, \frac{1}{4}, \frac{1}{8}, \frac{1}{2}, \frac{2}{4}$

B. $\frac{1}{8}, \frac{1}{2}, \frac{2}{8}, \frac{1}{8}, \frac{1}{4}$

C. $\frac{1}{2}, \frac{1}{8}, \frac{1}{4}, \frac{2}{16}, \frac{1}{8}$

SHOW YOUR WORK

The data below represents the height of students in Ms. Pegram's class. Use the data set to answer questions **3 - 6**

Student 1	Student 2	Student 3	Student 4	Student 5
$3\frac{1}{2}$ ft	$3\frac{1}{4}$ ft	$3\frac{1}{8}$ ft	$3\frac{1}{4}$ ft	$3\frac{3}{4}$ ft

3. Draw a line plot for the data set.

SHOW YOUR WORK

4. The tallest student is _____ feet taller than the shortest student.

SHOW YOUR WORK

5. What is the height of the two tallest students combined?

SHOW YOUR WORK

6. What is the most common height of all the students?

A. $3\frac{1}{2}$ ft

B. $3\frac{1}{4}$ ft

C. $3\frac{1}{8}$ ft

SHOW YOUR WORK

The line plot below represents the weight of newborn chicks in ounces. Use the line plot to answer questions 7 - 10

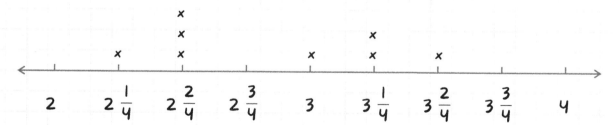

7. How much does the heaviest chick weigh?

A. $2\frac{1}{2}$

B. $3\frac{1}{4}$

C. $3\frac{1}{2}$

SHOW YOUR WORK

8. How much does the lightest chick weigh?

   A. $2\frac{1}{2}$

   B. $2\frac{1}{4}$

   C. 3

   SHOW YOUR WORK

9. What is the total weight of all the chicks? Show your work.

   SHOW YOUR WORK

10. If the total weight of all the chicks was redistributed evenly among each of the 8 chicks, how much would each chick weigh?

    SHOW YOUR WORK

We can use what we know about two dimensional shapes to find the volume of three dimensional objects.

What is volume?

Volume is the amount of space that an object occupies, or that is enclosed within a container.

How do you measure volume?

Volume can be measured with cubes like the one below. These cubes are called unit cubes because each one represents one cubic unit of volume.

unit cube

Even though we only see three faces of the cube, we can use our knowledge of shapes to recognize that the cube has **6** faces.

Consider the figure below.

How many cubes are represented in the figure?

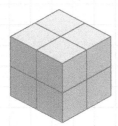

We only see **7** cubes, but we know there is a hidden cube holding up the starred block. When finding the volume of three dimensional shapes, we need to keep in mind that some of the cubes may not be visible once the shape is filled.

There are **8** cubes in the box.

Practice Questions

1. How many cubes are in the figure below?

SHOW YOUR WORK

2. How many cubes are in the figure below?

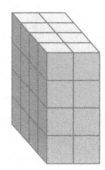

SHOW YOUR WORK

3. How many cubes are in the figure below?

SHOW YOUR WORK

4. How many cubes are in the figure below?

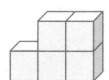

SHOW YOUR WORK

5. How many cubes are in the figure below?

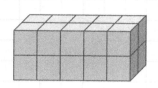

SHOW YOUR WORK

6. How many cubes will fit in the box (including the ones shown)?

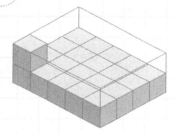

SHOW YOUR WORK

7. How many cubes will fit in the box (including the ones shown)?

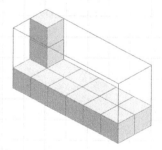

SHOW YOUR WORK

8. How many cubes will fit in the box (including the ones shown)?

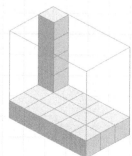

SHOW YOUR WORK

9. How many cubes will fit in the box (including the ones shown)?

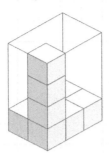

SHOW YOUR WORK

10. How many cubes will fit in the box (including the ones shown)?

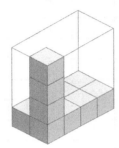

SHOW YOUR WORK

11. Sarah packed a box with 18 unit cubes. What is the volume of her box?

   A. 18 cubes

   B. 18 cubic units

   C. 18 units

SHOW YOUR WORK

12. Sarah packed a box with 21 unit cubes. What is the volume of her box?

   A. 21 cubes

   B. 21 cubic units

   C. 21 units

SHOW YOUR WORK

13. Sarah packed a box with **3** unit cubes. What is the volume of her box?

A. 3 cubes

B. 3 cubic units

C. 3 units

SHOW YOUR WORK

14. Paul packed a box with **2** rows of **2** unit cubes. How many unit cubes are in his box?

SHOW YOUR WORK

15. Willow packed a box with **3** rows of **2** unit cubes. How many unit cubes are in his box?

SHOW YOUR WORK

16. John packed a box with **10** rows of **12** unit cubes. How many unit cubes are in his box?

SHOW YOUR WORK

17. Kayla packed a box with 13 rows of 5 unit cubes. How many unit cubes are in her box?

SHOW YOUR WORK

18. Lila packed a box with 4 rows of 3 unit cubes. How many unit cubes are in her box?

SHOW YOUR WORK

19. Gordon packed a box with 7 rows of 9 unit cubes. How many unit cubes are in his box?

SHOW YOUR WORK

20. Paulo packed a box with 12 rows of 1 unit cubes. How many unit cubes are in his box?

SHOW YOUR WORK

Measuring Volume by Counting

We can use what we know about cubic units to calculate the volume of three dimensional shapes.

Let's look at Figure A.

cubic centimeter

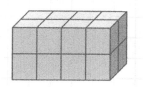

Figure A

Step 1: Count the Cubes

Even though we can't see every cube, we can apply our knowledge of shapes to determine how many cubes are in the figure. There are 4 rows of 4 cubes. There are 16 total cubes in Figure A.

16 cubes

Step 2: Look at the units

Notices that the unit cube is labeled cubic centimeter. That means that each cube represents one cubic centimeter. Be sure to check the units. They can be given in a variety of measurements, including centimeters, inches and feet.

centimeters

Step 3: Solve

Since each cube represents one cubic centimeter, and we have 16 cubes, the volume of Figure A is 16 cubic centimeters.

16 cubic centimeters   or   16 cm^3

Practice Questions

Use the figures below to answer questions 1 - 5. Each cube represents 1 cubic centimeter.

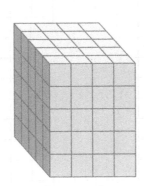

Figure A

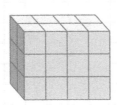

Figure B

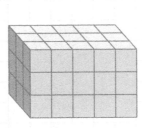

Figure C

1. What is the volume of the Figure A?

SHOW YOUR WORK

2. What is the volume of the Figure B?

SHOW YOUR WORK

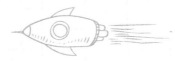

3. What is the volume of Figure C?

SHOW YOUR WORK

4. How much larger is the volume of Figure A than the volume of Figure C?

SHOW YOUR WORK

5. What is the volume of the Figure B and Figure C combined?

SHOW YOUR WORK

Use the figures below to answer questions 6 - 9. Each cube represents I cubic inch.

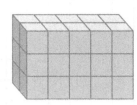 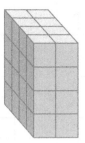

Figure A   Figure B   Figure C

6. Which Figure has the largest volume?

A. Figure A   SHOW YOUR WORK

B. Figure B

C. Figure C

7. Which Figure has the smallest volume?

A. Figure A   SHOW YOUR WORK

B. Figure B

C. Figure C

8. How much larger is the volume of Figure C than the volume of Figure A?

SHOW YOUR WORK

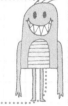

9. What is the volume of all the figures combined?

SHOW YOUR WORK

10. Draw a figure with a volume of **6** cubic feet

SHOW YOUR WORK

NOTES

Find the volume of a right rectangular prism

Sometimes we need to find the volume of a large shape. In this case, we don't want to spend time counting unit cubes individually. Luckily, there are formulas that we can use to calculate the volume of a rectangular prism more quickly.

Volume = length × width × height

Volume = base × height

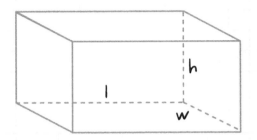

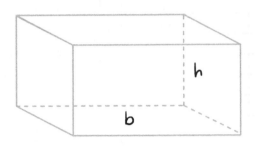

Let's look at an example.

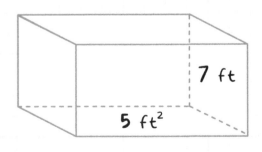

What is the volume of the rectangular prism?

The figure gives the base and height of the rectangular prism. We simply need to multiply the given units to find the volume.

Volume = base × height
___ = 5 × 7

The volume of the rectangular prism is 35 cm³

We can use what we know about unit cubes to check our answers.

Practice Questions

Use the figures below to answer questions 1 - 4.

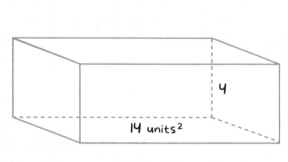

14 units²

Figure 1

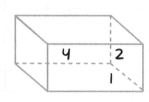

10
3
3

Figure 2

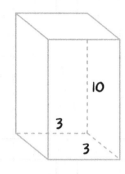

4   2
1

Figure 3

1. What is the volume of Figure 1?

SHOW YOUR WORK

2. What is the volume of Figure 2?

SHOW YOUR WORK

3. What is the volume of Figure 3?

SHOW YOUR WORK

4. How much larger is the volume of Figure 2 than the volume of Figure 1?

SHOW YOUR WORK

5. Angela used 1 centimeter cubes to build a tower. The tower was 5 cm long, 6 cm wide and 1 cm high. Which model represents her tower?

SHOW YOUR WORK

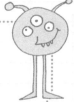

6. Kathleen bought a rectangular aquarium. It's **20** ft long, **10** ft wide and **5** ft high. It cost **$5** per cubic foot to fill the tank with water. How much does it cost to fill the entire tank with water?

A. $250

B. $500

C. $5,000

SHOW YOUR WORK

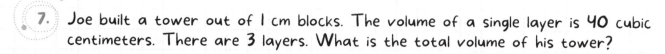

7. Joe built a tower out of 1 cm blocks. The volume of a single layer is **40** cubic centimeters. There are **3** layers. What is the total volume of his tower?

SHOW YOUR WORK

8. Emma receives four presents on her birthday. Each present has a base of 11 feet. Two of the boxes have a height of **2** feet. The other two boxes have a height of **3** feet. What is the total volume of the four presents combined?

SHOW YOUR WORK

9. Mr. Walker orders 3 boxes of books for his classroom. Each box has a base of **3** feet. Two of the boxes have a height on **5** feet. The other box has a height of **2** feet. What is the total volume of the three boxes combined?

SHOW YOUR WORK

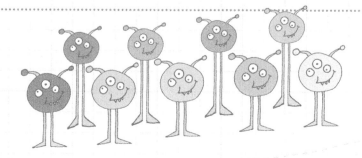

10. Nadeem built a tower out of 1 cm blocks. The volume of a single layer is **25** cubic centimeters. There are **6** layers. What is the total volume of his tower?

SHOW YOUR WORK

11. The present has a volume of **24** cubic centimeters. Which of the following could be the dimensions of the present?

A. 12 cm long x 12 cm wide x 1 cm high

B. 12 cm long x 10 cm wide x 2 cm high

C. 12 cm long x 2 cm wide x 1 cm high

SHOW YOUR WORK

12. Laura's package has a total volume of **1200** cubic cm. The package is **60** cm long and **10** cm wide. What is the height of the package?

A. 2 cm

B. 20 cm

C. 200 cm

SHOW YOUR WORK

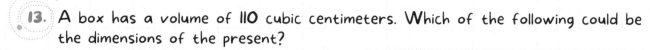

13. A box has a volume of 110 cubic centimeters. Which of the following could be the dimensions of the present?

SHOW YOUR WORK

A. 100 cm long x 5 cm wide x 5 cm high

B. 10 cm long x 11 cm wide x 1 cm high

C. 5 cm long x 20 cm wide x 10 cm high

14. Laura's package has a total volume of 400 cubic cm. The package is 20 cm long and 1 cm wide. What is the height of the package?

A. 2 cm

SHOW YOUR WORK

B. 20 cm

C. 200 cm

15. A box has a volume of 54 cubic feet. Which of the following could be the dimensions of the present?

SHOW YOUR WORK

A. 18 cm long x 3 cm wide x 1 cm high

B. 50 ft long x 4 ft wide x 1 ft high

C. 18 ft long x 3 ft wide x 1 ft high

Use the figures below to answer questions 16 - 20.

Each cube represents 1 cubic foot. Remember that some cubes may be hidden

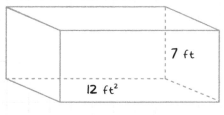

7 ft

12 ft²

Figure 1

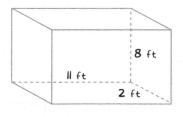

8 ft

11 ft

2 ft

Figure 2

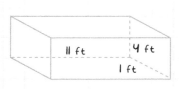

11 ft   4 ft

1 ft

Figure 3

16. What is the volume of Figure 1?

SHOW YOUR WORK

17. What is the volume of Figure 2?

SHOW YOUR WORK

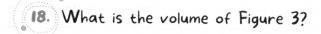

18. What is the volume of Figure 3?

SHOW YOUR WORK

19. How much larger is the volume of Figure 2 than the volume of Figure 3?

SHOW YOUR WORK

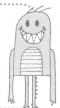

20. What is the total volume of all three figures?

SHOW YOUR WORK

Use the conversion chart below for questions 1 - 3

Conversion Chart			
Volume	Length	Weight	Time
1 gallon = 128 fluid ounces	1 kilometer = 1000 meters	1 kilogram = 1000 grams	1 year = 52 weeks
1 pint = 2 cups	1 mile = 5280 feet	1 ton = 2,000 pounds	1 week = 7 days
1 cup = 8 fluid ounces	1 yard = 3 feet	1 pound = 16 ounces	1 minute = 60 seconds

1. How many ounces are in **5 gallons**?

SHOW YOUR WORK

2. Convert **9 yards** into feet.

SHOW YOUR WORK

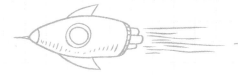

3. David swims **3** miles. His friend swims **2** miles. How many more feet does David swim than his friend?

A. 1

B. 650

C. 5,280

SHOW YOUR WORK

4. Quinn is making a cake. The recipe calls for **3** cups of milk. Quinn's measuring cup only displays ounces. If she follows the recipe, how many ounces of milk should she use for her cake?

A. 6

B. 24

C. 384

SHOW YOUR WORK

5. Javi is running a **5**-mile race. He has already run **2** miles. How many feet does he have left in the race?

SHOW YOUR WORK

The line plot shows the number of caterpillars, grouped by length to the nearest $\frac{1}{8}$ inch. Use the line plot to answer questions 4 - 7

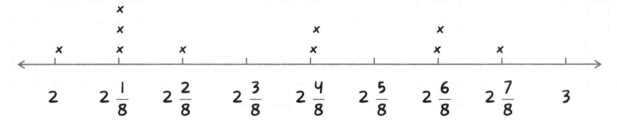

6. How much longer is the longest caterpillar than the shortest caterpillar?

SHOW YOUR WORK

7. What is the length of the three longest caterpillars combined?

SHOW YOUR WORK

8. If the length of all the caterpillars were combined and redistributed equally among all 10 caterpillars, how long would each caterpillar be?

SHOW YOUR WORK

9. If a new caterpillar is born $\frac{1}{8}$ the size of the shortest caterpillar, how many inches long will it be?

SHOW YOUR WORK

10. Avery builds a box that's 3 cubes high and 4 cubes wide. Carter builds one that's 6 cubes long and 2 cubes wide. Which box has the greater volume? Draw a picture to explain your answer.

SHOW YOUR WORK

11. Adele gives her brother two presents. Both presents have an area of 9 ft² and a height of 2 feet. What is the total volume of the two presents combined?

SHOW YOUR WORK

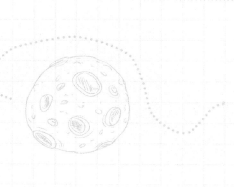

Use the figures below to answer questions 12 - 15.

Each cube represents 1 cubic unit. Remember that some cubes may be hidden.

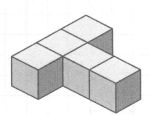

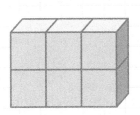

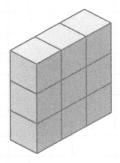

Figure 1   Figure 2   Figure 3

12. How many cubes are in Figure 1?

SHOW YOUR WORK

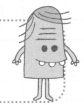

13. What is the volume of Figure 2?

SHOW YOUR WORK

14. What is the volume of Figure 3?

```
SHOW YOUR WORK
```

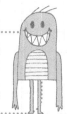

15. How much larger is the volume of Figure 3 than the volume of Figure 2?

```
SHOW YOUR WORK
```

Use the figures below to answer questions 16 - 20.

Each cube represents 1 cubic unit. Remember that some cubes may be hidden.

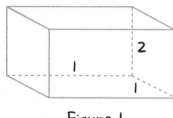

Figure 1

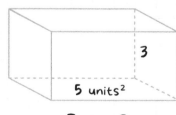

Figure 2

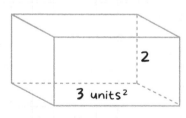

Figure 3

16. What is the volume of Figure 1?

```
SHOW YOUR WORK
```

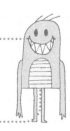

17. What is the volume of Figure **2**?

SHOW YOUR WORK

18. What is the volume of Figure **3**?

SHOW YOUR WORK

19. Which figure has the largest total volume?

A. Figure 1

B. Figure 2

C. Figure 3

D. The figures are equal

SHOW YOUR WORK

20. How much larger is the volume of Figure **2** than the volume of Figure **1**?

SHOW YOUR WORK

NOTES

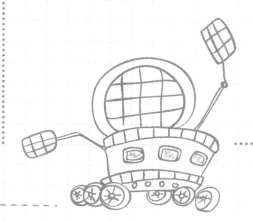

Chapter 5
Geometry

ARGOPREP
STUDY SMARTER, NOT HARDER

There are times when we need to read points on a coordinate plane.

What is a coordinate plane?
A coordinate plane is two number lines that intersect in the middle. The first number line is called the x-axis. It travels horizontally. The second number line is called the y-axis. It travels vertically. The number lines intersect at the origin.

How do you read a coordinate plane?
Each point on the plane is located with a set of coordinates called an ordered pair. The first number in the ordered pair tells you how far to travel across the x-axis from the origin. It's called the x-coordinate. The second number tells you how far to travel up the y-axis from the x-coordinate. It's called the y-coordinate.

Let's give it a try.

Which ordered pair represents Point A on the coordinate plane below?

A. (5, 2)

B. (2, 5)

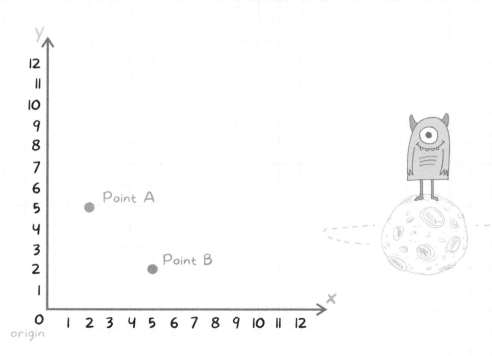

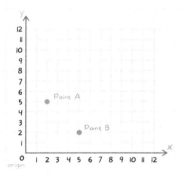

Step 1: Locate Point A

All of the points are labeled. We can see that Point A is red in the coordinate plane.

Step 2: Determine the x-coordinate

We know that the x-coordinate tells us how far to travel across the x-axis from the origin. So, we need to count how far Point A is from the origin.

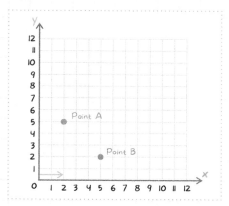

x-coordinate = 2

Step 3: Determine the y-coordinate

We know that the y-coordinate tells us how far to travel up the y-axis from the x-axis. So, we need to count how far Point A is from 2 on the x-axis.

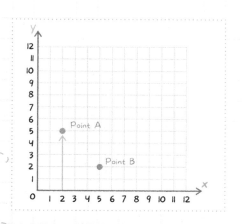

y-coordinate = 5

Step 4: **Write the ordered pair**

We know that the coordinates need to be presented in an ordered pair.

$$(x, y) \longrightarrow (2, 5)$$

NOTES

Practice Questions

Use the coordinate plane for questions 1 - 3

1. Point A is on the _____.

   A. origin

   B. x-axis

   C. y-axis

   D. all of the above

2. Point B is on the _____.

   A. origin

   B. x-axis

   C. y-axis

   D. all of the above

3. Point C is on the _____.

   A. origin

   B. x-axis

   C. y-axis

   D. all of the above

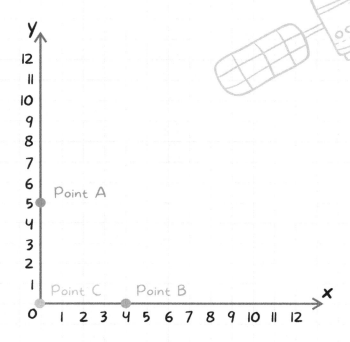

SHOW YOUR WORK

Use the coordinate plane for questions 4 - 5

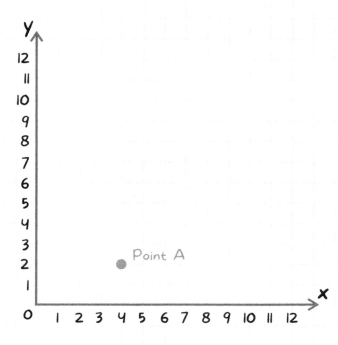

4. What is the y-coordinate of the point above?

   A. 4

   B. 2

   C. 6

   SHOW YOUR WORK

5. What is the x-coordinate of the point above?

   A. 4

   B. 2

   C. 6

   SHOW YOUR WORK

206

Use the coordinate plane for questions 6 - 7

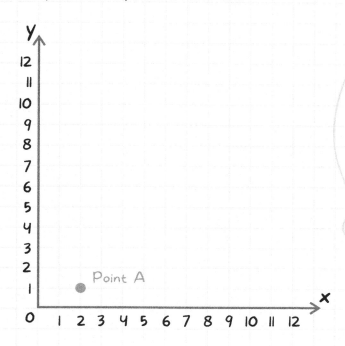

6. What is the y-coordinate of the point above?

A. 1

B. 2

C. 3

SHOW YOUR WORK

7. What is the x-coordinate of the point above?

A. 1

B. 2

C. 3

SHOW YOUR WORK

207

Use the coordinate plane for questions 11 - 15

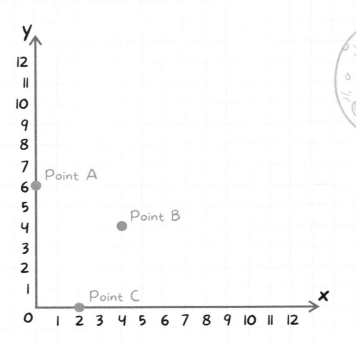

8. Write an ordered pair for Point A

> SHOW YOUR WORK

9. Write an ordered pair for Point B

> SHOW YOUR WORK

10. Write an ordered pair for Point C

> SHOW YOUR WORK

Use the coordinate plane for questions 11 - 15

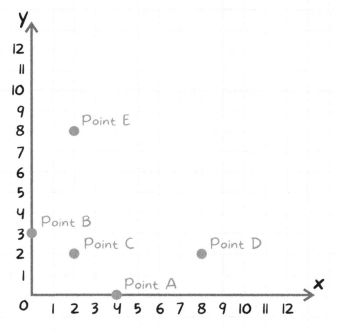

11. What are the coordinates of Point A?

> SHOW YOUR WORK

12. What are the coordinates of Point B?

> SHOW YOUR WORK

13. What are the coordinates of Point C?

> SHOW YOUR WORK

14. What are the coordinates of Point D?

> SHOW YOUR WORK

15. What are the coordinates of Point E?

> SHOW YOUR WORK

Graphing Points

Graphing points on a coordinate plane can help you analyze relationships between different sets of data. Consider the example below.

Graph the points on the coordinate plane using the chart below. What is the distance between the two points?

Point	Ordered Pair
A	(2, 3)
B	(2, 6)

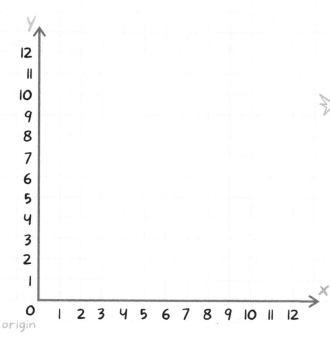

Step 1: Graph Point A

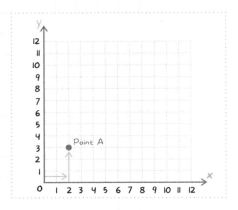

According to the chart, Point A has an ordered pair of (2, 3).

The ordered pair tells us to travel 2 points across the x-axis and 3 points up the y-axis.

Step 2: Graph Point B

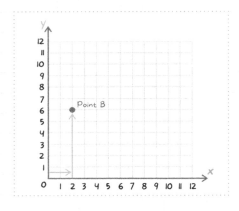

According to the chart, Point A has an ordered pair of (2, 6).

The ordered pair tells us to travel 2 points across the x-axis and 6 points up the y-axis.

Step 3: Analyze

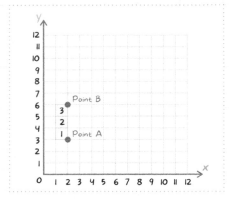

We can determine the distance between the two points by counting the number of units that fall in between them.

The distance between the two points is 3 units.

Practice Questions

Use the coordinate plane to answer questions 1 - 2

1. The four corners of a square are located at the points (3, 5), (3,8) (6,8) and (6,5). Plot the points to illustrate the square.

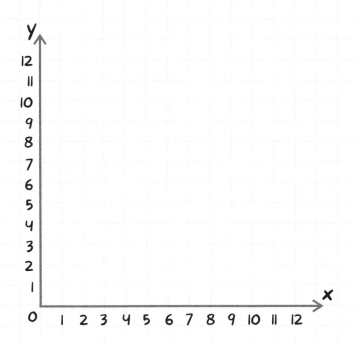

2. How long is each side of the square?

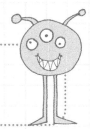

SHOW YOUR WORK

Use the coordinate plane to answer questions **3 - 6**.

John maps his friends houses on a coordinate plane. The axis represents miles.

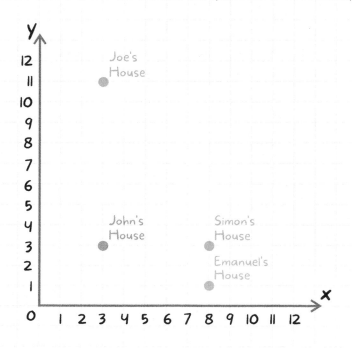

3. How far does John live from Simon?

A. 3 miles

B. 5 miles

C. 8 miles

SHOW YOUR WORK

4. Which friend lives closest to Simon?

A. John

B. Emanuel

C. Joe

SHOW YOUR WORK

5. Which friend lives farthest from John?

A. Joe

B. Simon

C. Emanuel

SHOW YOUR WORK

6. How far does Emanuel live from Simon?

A. 2 miles

B. 3 miles

C. 8 miles

SHOW YOUR WORK

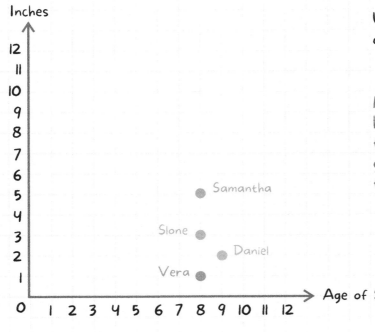

Inches

Age of Student

Use the coordinate plane to answer questions 7 - 11

Mr. Tompkins collected data on his students. The points show the age and number of inches grown since the beginning of the school year.

7. Who has grown the least since the beginning of the school year?

A. Vera

B. Slone

C. Daniel

D. Samantha

SHOW YOUR WORK

8. How many more inches did Samantha grow than Daniel?

A. 1

B. 2

C. 3

SHOW YOUR WORK

9. What is the total number of inches grown since the beginning of the school year?

A. 5 inches

B. 9 inches

C. 11 inches

SHOW YOUR WORK

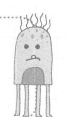

10. How old are most of the students in Mr. Tompkin's class?

A. 8

B. 9

C. 10

SHOW YOUR WORK

11. Who is the oldest student in Mr. Tompkin's class?

A. Vera

B. Sloane

C. Samantha

D. Daniel

SHOW YOUR WORK

Use the coordinate plane to answer questions 11 - 15

Heather's family is fishing. Each ordered pair shows the time of day and the number of fish caught.

Ordered Pair
(1, 2)
(3, 3)
(5, 6)
(7, 1)

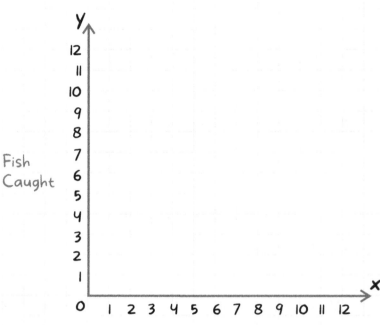

Fish Caught

Time of Day

12. Plot the points on the coordinate plane

13. How many total fish did Heather's family catch?

SHOW YOUR WORK

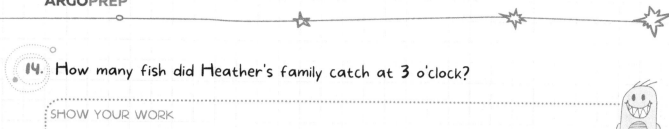

14. How many fish did Heather's family catch at **3** o'clock?

SHOW YOUR WORK

15. At what time did Heather's family catch the most fish?

SHOW YOUR WORK

NOTES

It's important to understand the different attributes of two-dimensional shapes. The chart below contains most of the shapes we need to be familiar with in **5th** grade.

Shape	Attributes	Image
Polygons	At least three straight sides	
Quadrilateral	Four straight sides	
Trapezoid	Four sides Only one pair of parallel sides	
Parallelogram	Four sides Opposite sides that are parallel	
Rhombus	Four sides Equal sides Parallel sides	
Rectangle	Four sides Four right angles	
Square	Four sides Equal sides Equal angles	

Let's see if we can match different shapes to their attributes!

Practice Questions

1. A square has 4 equal sides and ___ equal angles.

A. 2

B. 3

C. 4

SHOW YOUR WORK

2. A rhombus has 4 equal _____.

A. angles

B. sides

C. vertices

SHOW YOUR WORK

3. A _____ has only one pair of parallel sides

A. rectangle

B. trapezoid

C. parallelogram

SHOW YOUR WORK

4. A _____ has four equal sides

   A. rhombus

   B. trapezoid

   C. rectangle

SHOW YOUR WORK

5. A polygon is a closed shape with ___ or more straight segments?

   A. 1

   B. 2

   C. 3

   D. 4

SHOW YOUR WORK

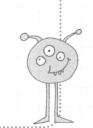

6. Draw two different quadrilaterals. Explain why your shapes are quadrilaterals.

SHOW YOUR WORK

7. Draw two shapes that are not quadrilaterals. Explain why your shapes are not quadrilaterals..

SHOW YOUR WORK

8. Draw two different parallelograms. Explain why your shapes are parallelograms.

SHOW YOUR WORK

9. Draw two shapes that are not parallelograms. Explain why your shapes are not parallelograms.

SHOW YOUR WORK

10. Draw a shape that is not a polygon. Explain why your shape is not a polygon.

SHOW YOUR WORK

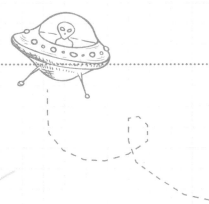

Classifying two-dimensional figures

Many two-dimensional objects can be categorized as more than one shape. For example, is the image below a square or rectangle?

At first, we may say the image is a square. However, it is also a rectangle. Take a look at the chart below.

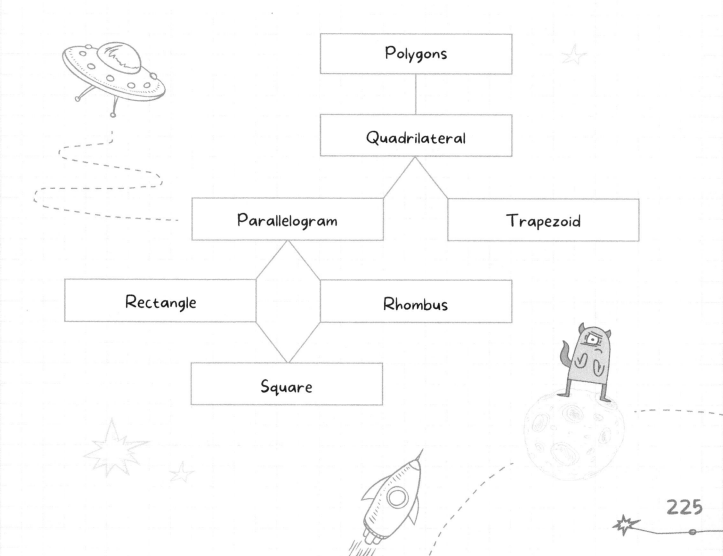

The chart shows how shapes can be organized into hierarchies based on their attributes.

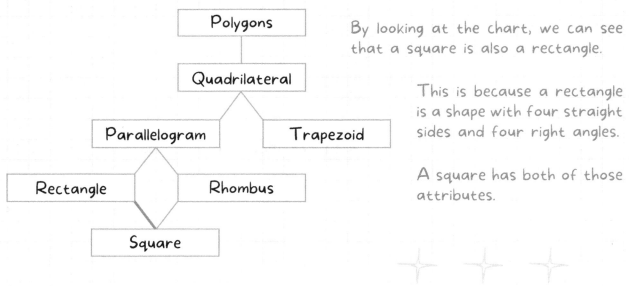

By looking at the chart, we can see that a square is also a rectangle.

This is because a rectangle is a shape with four straight sides and four right angles.

A square has both of those attributes.

Is a rectangle a square?

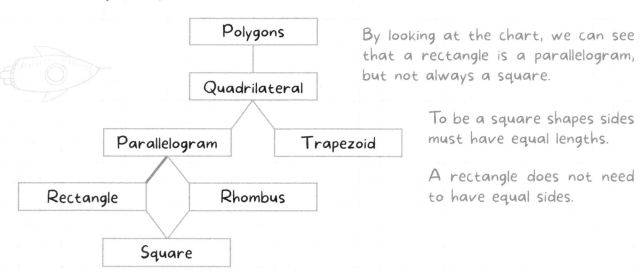

By looking at the chart, we can see that a rectangle is a parallelogram, but not always a square.

To be a square shapes sides must have equal lengths.

A rectangle does not need to have equal sides.

How do I organize shapes into a hierarchy?

In order to organize shapes into a hierarchy, you need to consider their attributes or properties. Let's practice!

Practice Questions

1. A square is _____ a rectangle. Explain your answer

A. Always

B. Sometimes

C. Never

SHOW YOUR WORK

2. A rhombus is _____ a square. Explain your answer

A. Always

B. Sometimes

C. Never

SHOW YOUR WORK

3. A parallelogram is _____ a rectangle. Explain your answer

A. Always

B. Sometimes

C. Never

SHOW YOUR WORK

4. Which two shapes are **not** squares? Circle and explain your answer.

SHOW YOUR WORK

227

5. Which shape is **not** parallelograms? Circle and explain your answer.

SHOW YOUR WORK

Use the chart and model below for questions 6 - 10

Square	Rhombus	Trapezoid	Quadrilateral
Parallelogram	Rectangle	Polygon	

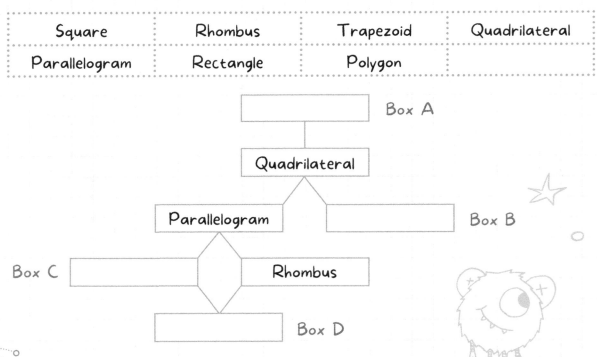

Box A

Quadrilateral

Parallelogram

Box B

Box C

Rhombus

Box D

6. Which shape goes in Box A?

A. Square

B. Polygon

C. Rectangle

SHOW YOUR WORK

7. Which shape goes in Box B?

A. Polygon

B. Rhombus

C. Trapezoid

SHOW YOUR WORK

8. Which shape goes in Box C?

A. Square

B. Polygon

C. Rectangle

SHOW YOUR WORK

9. Which shape goes in Box D?

A. Trapezoid

B. Rhombus

C. Square

SHOW YOUR WORK

10. Create a hierarchy that shows the relationship between different polygons.

SHOW YOUR WORK

1. Georgia earns $3 for every hour that she babysits. Use the coordinate plane to illustrate the amount of money she earns for babysitting 2, 3 and 4 hours.

SHOW YOUR WORK

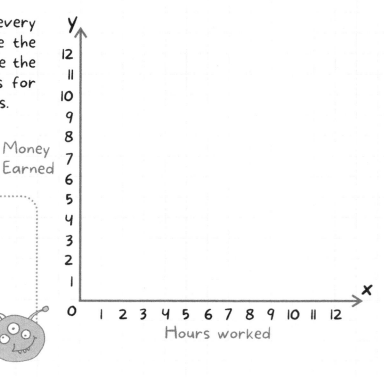

Money Earned

2. Jordan earns 2 hours of screen time for every hour she tutors her brother in math. Use the coordinate plane to illustrate the amount of screen time she earns for tutoring her brother for 2, 3 and 4 hours.

Screen Time Earned

SHOW YOUR WORK

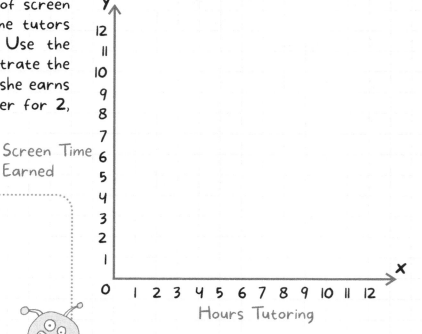

Use the coordinate plane below to answer questions 3 - 7

Amar is training for a marathon. Each ordered pair shows the time of day (x-coordinate) and the number of miles he ran (y-coordinate).

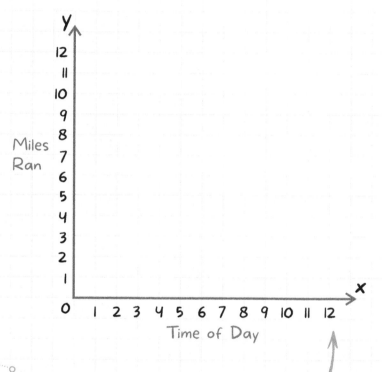

Ordered Pair
(2, 1)
(3, 4)
(4, 5)
(5, 1)

3. Plot the points on the coordinate plane.

4. What time of day does Amar run the farthest?

A. 2

B. 3

C. 4

D. 5

SHOW YOUR WORK

5. How much farther did Amar run at 3 than at 5?

A. 2

B. 3

C. 4

D. 5

SHOW YOUR WORK

6. What is the total distance Amar has run during his training?

SHOW YOUR WORK

7. At what two times does Amar run the same distance?

A. 2 and 3

B. 2 and 5

C. 3 and 4

D. 4 and 5

SHOW YOUR WORK

Use the coordinate plane for questions 8 - 10

8. What is the y-coordinate of Point C?

A. 0

B. 2

C. 8

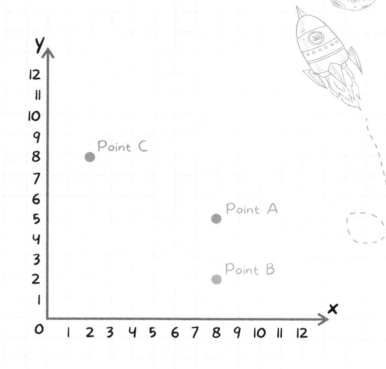

9. What is the x-coordinate of Point B?

A. 0

B. 2

C. 8

10. What is the distance between Point A and Point B?

A. 0

B. 3

C. 8

SHOW YOUR WORK

11. Which two shapes are rectangles? Circle and explain your answer.

SHOW YOUR WORK

12. Which two shapes are quadrilaterals? Circle and explain your answer.

SHOW YOUR WORK

13. Which shape is **not** a trapezoid? Circle and explain your answer.

SHOW YOUR WORK

14. Which shape is not a polygon? Circle and explain your answer.

SHOW YOUR WORK

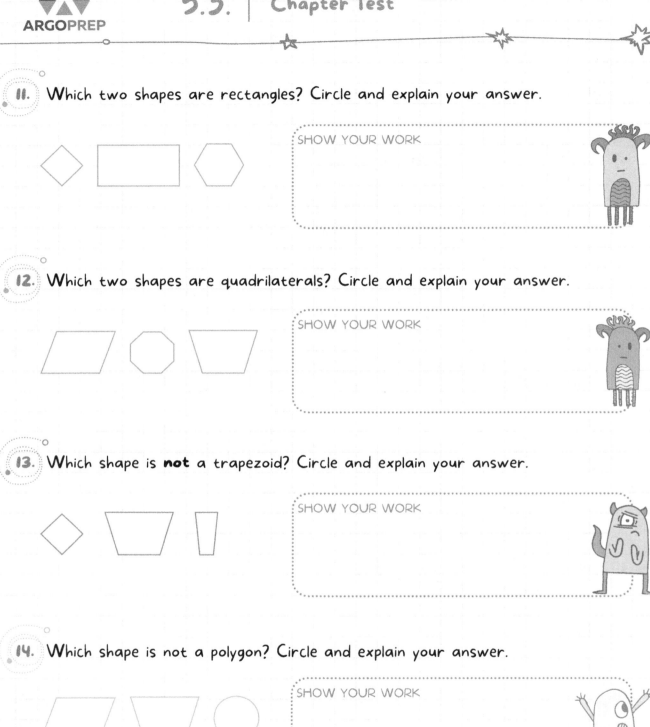

15. Which shapes are not a trapezoid? Circle and explain your answer.

SHOW YOUR WORK

Use the chart below to answer questions 15 - 20

Square	Rhombus	Trapezoid	Quadrilateral
Parallelogram	Rectangle	Polygon	

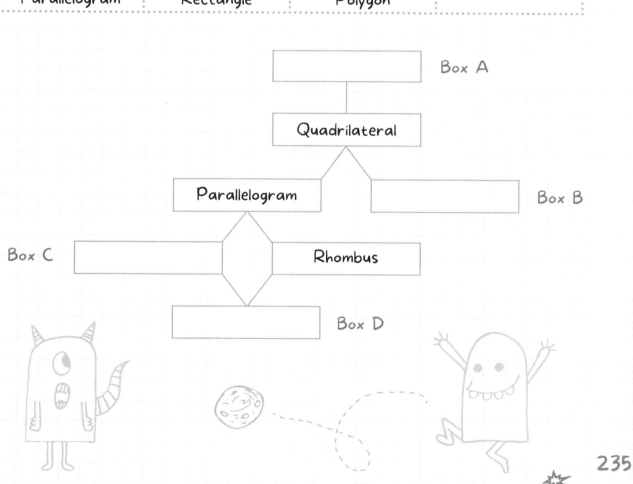

Box A

Quadrilateral

Parallelogram

Box B

Box C

Rhombus

Box D

16. Which shape goes in Box A?

A. Square

B. Polygon

C. Rectangle

SHOW YOUR WORK

17. Which shape goes in Box B?

A. Polygon

B. Rhombus

C. Trapezoid

SHOW YOUR WORK

18. Which shape goes in Box C?

A. Square

B. Polygon

C. Rectangle

SHOW YOUR WORK

19. Which shape goes in Box D?

A. Trapezoid

B. Rhombus

C. Square

SHOW YOUR WORK

20. Create your own hierarchy using the shapes in the chart below.

Square	Rhombus	Trapezoid	Quadrilateral
Parallelogram	Rectangle	Polygon	

SHOW YOUR WORK

Chapter 6 :
Mixed Assessment

1. Solve $4 \times [(16 - 3) + 1]$.

SHOW YOUR WORK

2. George swims 13 miles. Linus swims $\frac{1}{5}$ of the distance that George swims. How far does Linus swim?

SHOW YOUR WORK

3. Which part of the expression below should be calculated first? Explain your answer.

$$2 \times \{6 + [3 + 2 \times (9 - 7) + 3]\}$$

A. 2×6

B. $9 - 7$

C. $3 + 2$

D. 2×9

SHOW YOUR WORK

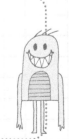

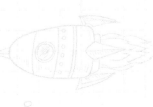

4. Which numerical expression has the same value as 6 + 2 × [(5 - 3) + 1)]

A. 6 × 2

B. 6 + 3

C. 8 × 3

D. 8 + 2

SHOW YOUR WORK

5. Write an expression that represents Twelve more than the product of 8 and 5.

SHOW YOUR WORK

6. Raven is buying groceries. The strawberries cost $1.25 per pound. How much will 5 pounds of strawberries cost?

SHOW YOUR WORK

7. The value of 8 in **26.842** is ___ times the value of the 8 in **75.789**

A. $\frac{1}{10}$

SHOW YOUR WORK

B. 10

C. 100

8. Kyle has $164.75. He buys 3 shirts for $24.50 each. He also buys a pair of shorts for $32.50. How much money does he have after his purchases?

A. $4.75

SHOW YOUR WORK

B. $58.75

C. $108

9. Jennifer is making cupcakes. She needs 1 $\frac{3}{4}$ cup of butter. She has $\frac{1}{16}$ cup of butter. How much more butter does she need if she wants to make cupcakes?

SHOW YOUR WORK

10. Carter gives his sister three presents. Two presents have a base of **4** ft² and a height of **2** feet. The other present has a length of **3** feet, a width of **1** foot and a height of **2** feet. What is the total volume of the three presents combined?

SHOW YOUR WORK

Use the conversion chart below for questions 11 - 15

Conversion Chart			
Volume	Length	Weight	Time
1 gallon = 128 fluid ounces	1 kilometer = 1000 meters	1 kilogram = 1000 grams	1 year = 52 weeks
1 pint = 2 cups	1 mile = 5280 feet	1 ton = 2,000 pounds	1 week = 7 days
1 cup = 8 fluid ounces	1 yard = 3 feet	1 pound = 16 ounces	1 minute = 60 seconds

11. Thomas is running a 10-mile race. He has already run **5** miles. How many feet does he have left in the race?

SHOW YOUR WORK

12. Mrs. Najera brings **6** gallons of water to field day. If she splits the gallons among **3** of the classes, how many ounces of water will each class get?

SHOW YOUR WORK

13. How many weeks are in **3** years? Use the conversion chart to calculate your answer.

SHOW YOUR WORK

14. Thea is making a pie. The recipe calls for **5** cups of milk. Thea has **80** ounces of milk. How many cups of milk will Thea have left after making her pies?

SHOW YOUR WORK

15. The zoo is transporting panda bears. Each panda weighs **200** pounds. Each vehicle can carry I ton. How many pandas can the zoo put on each vehicle?

SHOW YOUR WORK

16. $5\frac{3}{4} - 1\frac{1}{8} = \text{---}$

SHOW YOUR WORK

17. $\frac{1}{2} \times \frac{4}{5} = \text{---}$

SHOW YOUR WORK

18. Ryan receives a present that's **5** inches long and **4** inches wide. Sloane receives one that's **4** inches long and **5** inches wide. Which present has the greater area? Draw a picture to explain your answer.

SHOW YOUR WORK

19. The picture below represents **3 + 3**. Draw a picture that represents **(3 + 3) × 3**.

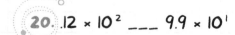

SHOW YOUR WORK

20. $.12 \times 10^2$ ___ 9.9×10^1

A. >   SHOW YOUR WORK

B. <

C. =

21. 5.890 ___ 5.89

A. >   SHOW YOUR WORK

B. <

C. =

22. $12 \times \dfrac{3}{4}$ ___ 12. How can you tell without multiplying?

A. >   SHOW YOUR WORK

B. <

C. =

23. 1.89×10^2 ___ 12×10

A. >   SHOW YOUR WORK

B. <

C. =

24. Write 121.10 in expanded form.

SHOW YOUR WORK

25. 51.66 ÷ 8.2 = ___ Show your work.

SHOW YOUR WORK

26. 8 hundredths × $\frac{1}{10}$ =

A. 8 thousandths

B. 8 tenths

C. 8 tens

D. 8 thousands

SHOW YOUR WORK

27. Round 3.998 to the nearest whole number.

SHOW YOUR WORK

28. Lara swims **32** laps a day. How many laps does she swim in **7** days?

SHOW YOUR WORK

29. 12 people want to share 15 pies. How much pie will each person get?

SHOW YOUR WORK

30. Angelica is making punch. Each serving takes $\frac{2}{3}$ cups of pineapple juice. If Angelica

has **6** cups of pineapple juice, how many servings of punch can she make? Use a model to represent the equation.

SHOW YOUR WORK

Use the coordinate plane and chart for questions 31 - 34

Hours Reading	Screen Time
3	
6	
9	
12	

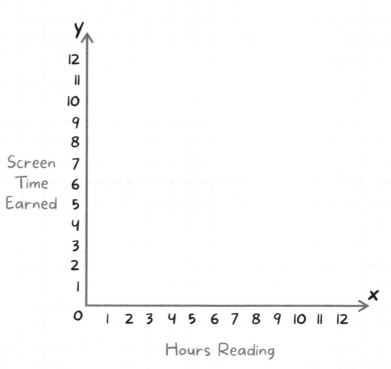

31. Isabella earns 1 hour of screen time for every 3 hours that she reads. Complete the chart above to show how much screen time she earns after 3, 6, 9 and 12 hours of reading.

32. Plot the ordered pairs on the coordinate plane.

33. Write a rule for the ordered pairs.

SHOW YOUR WORK

34. How many hours of screen time will Isabella have earned after reading for 15 hours?

SHOW YOUR WORK

35. Lars is stacking blocks.

- He starts by stacking **22** blocks
- **13** of his blocks get knocked over
- He adds **9** more blocks to his stack
- $\frac{1}{3}$ of the remaining piles blow away

How many blocks does Lars have in his stack at the end of the sequence?

SHOW YOUR WORK

The line plot represents the length of butterfly wingspans in inches. Use the line plot for questions **36 - 39**.

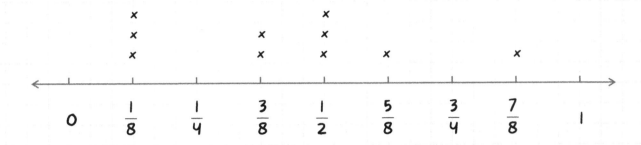

36. How many inches is the longest wingspan?

> SHOW YOUR WORK

37. How many more inches is the longest wingspan from the second longest wing span?

> SHOW YOUR WORK

38. How many butterflies have a wingspan of $\frac{1}{2}$ inch?

> SHOW YOUR WORK

39. How many inches is all of the wingspans combined?

SHOW YOUR WORK

Use the graph below to answer questions **40 - 45**.

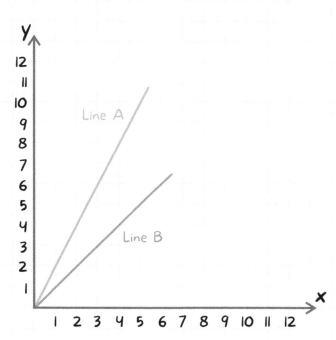

The graph shows y, the total cost in dollars, for x scoops of ice cream.

Line A represents chocolate ice cream.

Line B represents vanilla ice cream.

40. Based on the information in the graph, which type of ice cream is more expensive? Explain your reasoning.

SHOW YOUR WORK

41. What rule is used to represent Line A?

    A. $y = x + 2$

    B. $y = x - 2$

    C. $y = x \times 2$

SHOW YOUR WORK

42. Write a rule to represent Line B.

SHOW YOUR WORK

43. Which statement describes the relationship between Line A and Line B?

    A. The lines are parallel

    B. The y-coordinates on line A are two times the size of the y-coordinates on line B

    C. The y-coordinates on line B are two times the size of the y-coordinates on line A

    D. The lines are equal

SHOW YOUR WORK

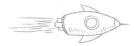

44. Hannah has **$10**. If she buys **3** scoops of chocolate ice cream, how much money will she have left?

SHOW YOUR WORK

45. Daniel buys **2** scoops of vanilla ice cream and **1** scoop of chocolate ice cream. How much money did he spend on ice cream?

SHOW YOUR WORK

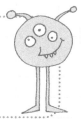

46. Write **.789** in expanded form.

SHOW YOUR WORK

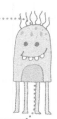

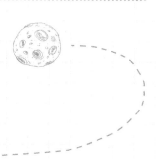

47. Write 1.3 in expanded form.

> SHOW YOUR WORK

Use the figures below to answer questions 48 - 51. Each cube represents 1 cubic centimeter.

Figure A   Figure B   Figure C

 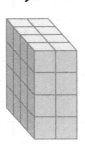 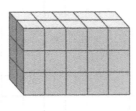

48. Which figure has the largest volume?

> SHOW YOUR WORK

49. What is the volume of all the figures combined?

> SHOW YOUR WORK

50. How much larger is the volume of Figure C than the volume of Figure A?

SHOW YOUR WORK

51. Use cubic centimeter cubes to draw a figure with a volume smaller than Figure B.

SHOW YOUR WORK

52. Select the expression that represents (12 + 2) ÷ 2

A. The product of 12 and 2, divided by 2

B. The quotient of 12 and 2, divided by 2

C. The sum of 12 and 2, divided by 2

D. The difference of 12 and 2, divided by 2

SHOW YOUR WORK

53. 8 people want to share 6 cupcakes. What fraction of cupcake will each person receive?

> SHOW YOUR WORK

54. Joelle donated 34 packs of erasers to his school. Each pack contained 240 erasers. How many total erasers did Joelle donate to his school?

> SHOW YOUR WORK

55. What is another way to write 2.05×10^3?

A. 20.5

B. 205

C. 2,050

D. 20,500

> SHOW YOUR WORK

Use the figures below to answer questions **56 - 60**. Measurements are given in feet.

Figure A

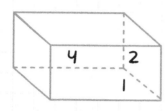

4
2
1

Figure B

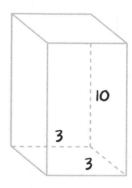

10
3
3

Figure C

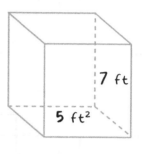

7 ft
5 ft²

56. Which Figure has the largest volume?

A. Figure A

B. Figure B

C. Figure C

SHOW YOUR WORK

57. Which Figure has the smallest volume?

A. Figure A

B. Figure B

C. Figure C

SHOW YOUR WORK

58. How much larger is the volume of Figure C than the volume of Figure A?

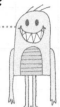

SHOW YOUR WORK

59. What is the volume of all the figures combined?

SHOW YOUR WORK

60. Draw a figure with a volume larger than Figure A, Figure B and Figure C.

SHOW YOUR WORK

61. There are 148 students at field day. Each class has 18 students. How many classes are there at field day?

A. 6

B. 7

C. 8

D. 9

SHOW YOUR WORK

62. 1008 ÷ 24 = ___ Use an area model to solve the equation.

SHOW YOUR WORK

63. What is $\frac{1}{8}$ of 16?

A. $\frac{1}{2}$

B. 2

C. 20

SHOW YOUR WORK

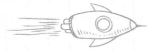

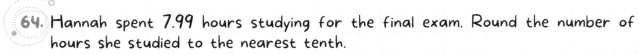

64. Hannah spent 7.99 hours studying for the final exam. Round the number of hours she studied to the nearest tenth.

SHOW YOUR WORK

65. Kylie went to the mall last weekend. She spent $3\frac{1}{2}$ hours shopping. She spent $\frac{1}{3}$ of that time at the food court. How many hours did Kylie spend at the mall?

SHOW YOUR WORK

66. Which number represents the expression?

$$(2 \times 1000) + (4 \times 100) + (4 \times 10) + (6 \times \frac{1}{10})$$

A. 2446

B. 2,440.6

C. 20,440.6

SHOW YOUR WORK

67. $10 \times 150 =$

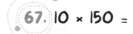

SHOW YOUR WORK

68. $250 \times \dfrac{1}{10} =$

SHOW YOUR WORK

Use the model below to answer questions 69 - 71.

1	1	1	1	$\frac{1}{4}$
1	1	1	1	$\frac{1}{4}$
1	1	1	1	$\frac{1}{4}$
1	1	1	1	$\frac{1}{4}$

69. The rectangle is ___ units long.

A. 4

B. $4\frac{1}{4}$

C. 5

SHOW YOUR WORK

70. The rectangle is ___ units wide.

A. 4

B. $4\frac{1}{4}$

C. 5

SHOW YOUR WORK

71. The area of the rectangle is ___ units².

Use the model below to answer questions 72 - 74.

1	1	$\frac{1}{2}$
1	1	$\frac{1}{2}$

72. The rectangle is ___ units long.

A. 2

B. $2\frac{1}{2}$

C. 5

SHOW YOUR WORK

73. The rectangle is ___ units wide.

A. 2

B. $2\frac{1}{2}$

C. 5

SHOW YOUR WORK

74. The area of the rectangle is ___ units².

> SHOW YOUR WORK

The data below represents the lengths of different ribbon. Use the data set to answer questions **75 - 78**.

Red	Orange	Yellow	Green	Blue
$2\frac{1}{4}$ ft	$2\frac{3}{4}$ ft	$2\frac{1}{8}$ ft	$2\frac{1}{4}$ ft	$2\frac{3}{4}$ ft

75. Draw a line plot for the data set.

> SHOW YOUR WORK

76. The longest ribbon is ___ feet longer than the shortest ribbon.

> SHOW YOUR WORK

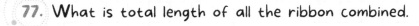

77. What is total length of all the ribbon combined.

SHOW YOUR WORK

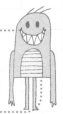

78. If the length of all the ribbon combined was redistributed equally among each of the **5** colors, how long would each color be?

SHOW YOUR WORK

79. Write 10.45 in expanded form.

SHOW YOUR WORK

80. Which numerical expression is five times larger than (17 - 5) × 9

A. (17 - 5) × 9 × 5

B. (17 + 5) ÷ (9 × 5)

C. 5 × (17 - 5) ÷ 9

D. [(17 - 5) × 9] × 5

SHOW YOUR WORK

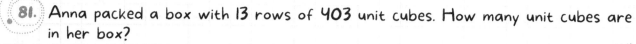

81. Anna packed a box with 13 rows of 403 unit cubes. How many unit cubes are in her box?

SHOW YOUR WORK

82. Jake packed a box with 105 rows of 12 unit cubes. How many unit cubes are in his box?

SHOW YOUR WORK

83. Kira packed a box with 135 rows of 15 unit cubes. How many unit cubes are in her box?

SHOW YOUR WORK

84. 65 + 26.25 = ___. Show your work.

A. 67.25

B. 91.25

C. 124.25

SHOW YOUR WORK

85. Which problem could be solved with the expression 4 × (5 + 2)?

A. Nelson orders **5** chocolate chip cookies and **2** sugar cookies. He spends **4** dollars on each. How many cookies does he buy?

B. Christina buys **5** graphic novels and **2** nonfiction texts. She reads the books **4** times a week. How many hours does she read each week?

C. Mary swims **4** times a week. She swims **5** laps of backstroke each of those mornings and **2** laps of freestyle each of those mornings. How many laps does she swim each week?

SHOW YOUR WORK

86. 12.6 × 4.5 =

SHOW YOUR WORK

87. Susan spent $5\frac{1}{2}$ hours preparing for the dinner party. She spent $\frac{1}{3}$ of that time cleaning the house. How many hours did Susan spend cleaning her house?

SHOW YOUR WORK

88. $\frac{1}{2} + \frac{1}{4} + \frac{1}{3} =$ ___ Show your work

SHOW YOUR WORK

89. 410.15 - 2.45 =

SHOW YOUR WORK

90. Which shape is a square? Circle and explain your answer.

SHOW YOUR WORK

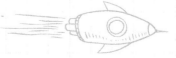

91. Which shape is **not** a polygon? Circle and explain your answer.

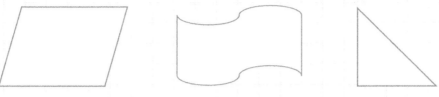

SHOW YOUR WORK

92. A rhombus is a square.

A. Always

B. Sometimes

C. Never

SHOW YOUR WORK

93. A circle is a polygon.

A. Always

B. Sometimes

C. Never

SHOW YOUR WORK

94. A square is a rhombus.

A. Always

B. Sometimes

C. Never

SHOW YOUR WORK

95. A triangle is a parallelogram.

A. Always

B. Sometimes

C. Never

SHOW YOUR WORK

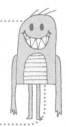

96. When multiplied by $\frac{1}{2}$ is 13 scaled up or down? Explain your answer.

SHOW YOUR WORK

97. Which number is more than 127? How can you tell without multiplying?

A. $127 \times \frac{1}{2}$

B. $127 \times \frac{2}{2}$

C. $127 \times \frac{2}{1}$

SHOW YOUR WORK

98. Kara runs 13 miles. Brett runs $\frac{3}{5}$ of the distance Kara runs. How far does Brett run?

SHOW YOUR WORK

99. $18 \times \frac{3}{4} = \_\_\_$

SHOW YOUR WORK

100. $5\frac{3}{8} + \frac{3}{4} = \_\_\_$

SHOW YOUR WORK

NOTES

ANSWER SHEET

Chapter 1:

1.1.A Evaluate Numerical Expressions with ( ), { } and [ ]

1. 17. First, calculate 3 × 4 = 12. Then add 5.
2. D. Parentheses should be solved before brackets or braces.
3. (7 + 8) × 3 = 45. First, calculate 7 + 8 = 15. Then, multiply by 3.
4. 22. First, calculate (8 - 3) = 5. Then add 5 + 6. The multiply 11 × 2.
5. B. Both expressions are equal to 29.
6. D. According to the order of operations, parentheses should be solved before brackets or braces.
7. The statement is incorrect. (7 - 3) + 6 × 2 = 16. First calculate (7 - 3) = 4. Then calculate 6 × 2 = 12. Then add 4 to 12.
8. (24 + 6) ÷ 3 = 10. First calculate (24 + 6) = 30 because the operation is in parentheses. Then divide by 3.
9. (54 ÷ 6) - 3 = 6. First calculate 54 ÷ 6 = 9. Then subtract 3.
10. The statement is incorrect. 6 + 36 ÷ (3 × 2) - 3 = 9. First, calculate (3 × 2) = 6. Then divide 36 ÷ 6 = 6. Then calculate 6 + 6 - 3 = 9
11. 68. First calculate (7 × 2) = 14. Then calculate (9 × 6) = 54. Add the two sums to get 68.
12. The statement is true. 4 + 8 × (6 - 4) = 20. First, calculate (6 - 4) = 2. Then calculate 8 × 2 = 16. Then calculate add 4.
13. C. Both expressions are equal to 36.
14. 12. First, calculate (8 - 6) = 2. Then multiply 6 × 2 = 12. Then divide 12 + 3. Finally, add. 8.
15. (60 ÷ 2) + 6 - 3 = 33. First calculate (60 ÷ 2) = 30. Then calculate 30 + 6 - 3.

1.1.B Write Numerical Expressions

1. (12 + 4) ÷ 2
2. C. Operations in parentheses should be calculated first. Sum means the result of adding two numbers.
3. B. It's a comparison problem with parentheses. First, add 6 laps and 9 laps. Then, multiply by three.

4. D. It's a comparison problem. The original expression is multiplied by 10.

5. (12 - 3) × 3   or   3 × (12 - 3). First represent the number of cookies Marisol has after her brother eats 3. Next, represent the number of cookies her father helps her bake.

6. 5 × (6 ÷ 3)   or   (6 ÷ 3) × 5. It's a comparison problem. The quotient (division) needs to be calculated first.

7. A. Quotient is the result of division. Doubled means to multiply by 2.

8. (1 × 7) × 3. It's a comparison problem. First represent the number of glasses Ben drinks (1 glass of milk times 7 days a week). Then, multiply by 3.

9. C. Use parentheses and brackets to ensure the order of operations matches the sequence described.

10. D. 4 more than 3 is an addition statement. 9 times that sum is a multiplication statement.

11. Answers may vary, but should represent 4 times the original equation. For example:

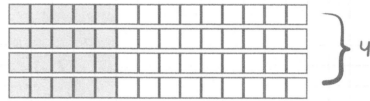

12. 3 × (5 + 3)   or   (5 + 3) × 3. It's a comparison problem. The addition needs to be calculated first.

13. {[(6 + 2) × 3] + 2} × 4   or   4 × {[(6 + 2) × 3] + 2}. Use braces to ensure the original expression is calculated before multiplying by 4.

14. (12 + 4) ÷ 2. To express the sum of 12 and 4, we use addition. To represent half, we divide by 2..

15. A. The difference between 9 and 3 represents (9 - 3). Twice as many represents the multiplication.

1.2. Analyze patterns and relationships

1. Sequence **2** is **3** times the size of Sequence 1.

Rule: Add 2	Rule: Add 6
2	6
4	12
6	18
8	24

2. A. The rule is add **3** for both the x- and y-coordinates.

3. y is **2** more than x   or   y = x + **2**. The coordinate pairs are created using the numbers in the x and y columns.

Point	X	Y	(x, y)
A	1	3	(1, 3)
B	3	5	(3, 5)
C	6	8	(6, 8)
D	9	11	(9, 11)

4. B. First list the ordered pairs. Then, determine the relationship.

5. The first number in each coordinate pair tells you how far to travel on the x-axis. The second number tells you how far to travel up the the y-axis. Do this for both points.

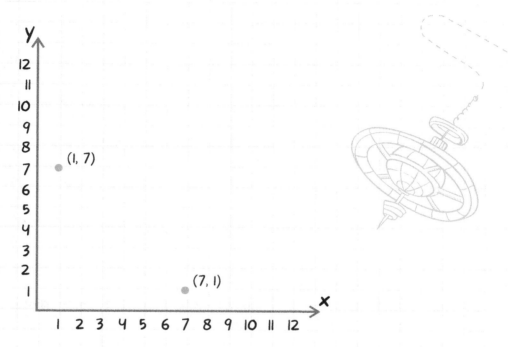

6. C. Each x-coordinate is doubled to determine the y-coordinate. $y = x \times 2$

7. Determine the pattern between the x and y-coordinate to complete the chart. y is x multiplied by itself or $y = x^2$

X	Y	(x, y)
3	9	(3, 9)
5	25	(5, 25)
7	49	(7, 49)
9	81	(9, 81)

8. The line intersects at the points below. The x-coordinates increase by **2**. The y-coordinates decrease by **3**.

x	y
0	9
2	6
4	3
6	0

9. Add **2** to the numbers in the x column to get the number for the y column.

x	y
5	7
7	9
9	11

10. B. Multiply by **2** and add 1.

11. C. Find three on the x-axis to determine the y-coordinate. The y-coordinate represents the price for **3** scoops.

12. Determine the relationship to complete the chart.
    The relationship is y = (3 × x) + 1

x	y
2	7
3	10
4	13

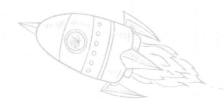

13. Plot the points to determine the pattern. Over one on the x-axis, up one on the y-axis. The remaining coordinate pairs are (9, 5) and (10, 6)

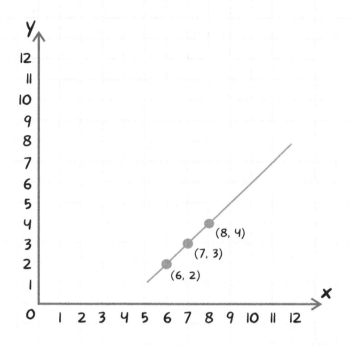

14. y = x ÷ 2. The y-coordinate is determined by dividing each x-coordinate by 2.

15. Strawberries are more expensive than blueberries.
Look at 1 on the x-axis. This represents one berry. Next travel up the y-axis to see the cost of one berry. The blueberry intersects at 2, representing **2** dollars. The strawberry line intersects at 3, representing **3** dollars.

1.3. Chapter Test

1. 90. First calculate (27 - 19) = 8. Then calculate [8 + 2] = 10. Then calculate 9 × 10.
2. (6 × 3) - 8. The product of 6 and 3 can be represented as 6 × 3.
   Since the product needs to be calculated first, we place parentheses around the operation before adding - 8 to the expression.
3. C. Both expressions equal 21.
4. A. List the points as ordered pairs to help you see the pattern.

Graph 1

x	y
0	4
1	5
2	6
3	7

Graph 2

x	y
0	2
1	3
2	4
3	5

5. Use the graph to support your thinking.

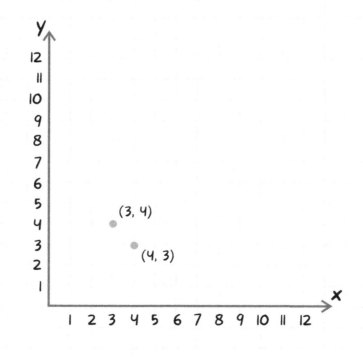

(3, 4)

(4, 3)

6. She makes her first mistake in step **3**. She should complete the operation in the braces before dividing.

7. C. Determine the pattern to see which coordinates would appear on the line. The pattern is $y = x \times 2$

8. **4** . First calculate $(17 - 2) = 5$ and $(22 \div 2) = 11$. Then calculate $5 + 11 = 16$. Then divide **16** by **4**.

9. The expression is three times as large as the original table.

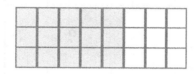

10. B. A quotient is the result of two numbers divided.

11. Ginger snaps are more expensive.
Look at I on the x-axis. This represents one cookie. Next travel up the y-axis to see the cost of one cookie. The chocolate chip cookie intersects at I, representing I dollar. The ginger snap line intersects at **3**, representing **3** dollars.

12. B. We can tell by looking at the chart that the y-coordinate is always the same value as the x-coordinate. (1, 1) (2, 2) (3, 3) (4, 4), etc.

13. $y = x \times 3$ or   multiply by **3**. Locate the coordinate pairs on the graph to determine the rule.

14. B. Look at I on the x-axis. This represents one cookie. Next travel up the y-axis to see the cost of one cookie. The chocolate chip cookie intersects at I, representing I dollar. The ginger snap line intersects at **3**, representing **3** dollars. This pattern coninues.

15. C. Use parentheses and brackets to ensure the order of operations matches the sequence described. Remember that we divide by **2** to get half.

16. C. **4** hours of math plus **3** hours of social studies each day. Since there are **7** days in one week, we multiply by **7**.

17. D. Multiply the original expression by **6**. Use brackets to keep the original expression together.

18. B. The product is the result of multiplying two numbers. Use parentheses to ensure the order of operations matches the sequence described.

19. y = x + 5

x	y	(x,y)
1	6	(1, 6)
2	7	(2, 7)
3	8	(3, 8)
4	9	(4, 9)

20. (6 + 9) ÷ 3. Use parentheses and brackets to ensure the order of operations matches the sequence described.

Chapter 2:

2.1.A Understand the Place Value System

1. B. The place value shifts to the right.
2. B. The 9 is in the tens place.
3. C. 5 hundreds is equivalent to 500. When we multiply by 10 we shift the place value to the left, which would give us 5,000. This can be expressed as 5 hundreds × 10.
4. A. The 3 is to the right of the 6. That means it's value is $\frac{1}{10}$ the value.
5. A. 3 hundredths is .003. Shift the place value to the right when you multiply by $\frac{1}{10}$. This gives us .003, which can be expressed 3 thousandths.
6. C. The 4 is to the left of the 8. That means it's value is 10 times larger.
7. C. 7 tens is 70. Dividing by 10 is the same as multiplying by $\frac{1}{10}$. So, we shift the place value to the right one time. This gives us 7, which can be expressed 7 ones.

8. 34,500. You can use what you've learned about place value to solve the problem. Since we are multiplying by 10, the digits shift to the right.
9. A. 4 is in the hundreds place, which can be expressed as 4 hundreds or 400.
10. 1,872.6. You can use what you've learned about place value to solve the problem. Since we are dividing by 10, the digits shift to the right.

2.1.B Place Value and Powers of Ten

1. C. Place value shifts to the left one time.

2. B. Place value shifts to the right 2 times.
3. D. Place value shifts to the left two times.
4. C. Place value shifts to the right 3 times.
5. B. 10^4 is equivalent to $10 \times 10 \times 10 \times 10$, which can be expressed as 10,000.
6. D. Place value of 10 shifts to the left three times.
7. B. 100 can be expressed as 10^2, which is equivalent to 10×10.
8. 7,200,000. Place value shifts to the left 6 times.
9. D. 10^4 is equivalent to ten multiplied 4 times, which can be expressed as $10 \times 10 \times 10 \times 10$.
10. B. 10^2 is equivalent to ten multiplied 2 times, which can be expressed as 10×10 or 100.

2.1.C Read, write, and compare decimals to thousandths

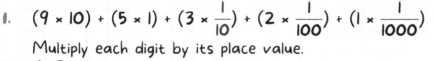

1. $(9 \times 10) + (5 \times 1) + (3 \times \frac{1}{10}) + (2 \times \frac{1}{100}) + (1 \times \frac{1}{1000})$
    Multiply each digit by its place value.
2. A. Each digit is multiplied by its place value.
3. B. The tenths place makes it less than.
4. C. Each digit is multiplied by its place value.
5. C. The zero in the hundredths place does not change the value of the first number.
6. C. Rewrite each number in standard form and use the place value chart to determine which number is greater.
7. B. .030 > .300. Use the place value chart to determine which number is greater.

8. B. Use the place value chart to express each digit in standard form.
9. B. Use the place value chart to determine which number is greater. The ones place is to the left of the tenths place.
10. C. Each number represents a different place value.
11. B. 3 hundredths < 30. Use the place value chart to determine which number is greater. Hundredths is less than tens.

12. $(8 \times 10) + (2 \times 1) + (6 \times \frac{1}{10}) + (7 \times \frac{1}{100}) + (5 \times \frac{1}{1000})$

Multiply each digit by its place value.

13. A. Use the place value chart to determine which number is greater.
14. C. **534.6** is written in word form.

15. $(6 \times 1) + (3 \times \frac{1}{10}) + (7 \times \frac{1}{100}) + (3 \times \frac{1}{1000})$. Multiply each digit by its place value.

16. B. Use the place value chart to determine which number is greater.
17. A. Use the place value chart to determine which number is greater.
18. B. The other two numbers are equal to 3.14
19. C. Use the place value chart to determine which number is greater. The numbers are equal.
20. A. Use the place value chart to determine how to rewrite the number.

2.1.D Rounding decimals

1. **2.570.** The 6 is in the hundredths place. The number to its right is greater than 4, so you round up.
2. B. The **3** is in the ones place. The number to its right is greater than 4, so you round up.
3. **6.7530.** The 3 is in the thousandths place. The number to its right is less than 4, so you round down.
4. B. **2** is the whole number. The number to its right greater than 4, so you round up.
5. **5.8.** The number to its right is less than 4, so you round up.
6. D. **96.09** is rounded to **96**.

7. **299.** The 8 is in the tens place. The number to its right is greater than 4. The number is rounded up to **299.**
8. **8.90.** The 9 is in the hundredths place. The number to its right is greater than 4. You need to round up to ten, which changes the number in the tenths place.
9. **A. 24.05** is rounded to **24.**
10. **768.760.** The 5 is in the hundredths place. The number to its right is less than 4, so you round up.

2.2.A Multiplying Multi-Digit Whole Numbers

1. **2,010**
2. **D.** Calcuate **32 × 12** since there are 12 cupcakes in a dozen.
3. **4,368**
4. He multiplied the product of 542 × 10 by 2. He should have multiplied 542 by 2 and then added the two products. The solution is **6,504.**
5. **392.** Calculate **28 × 14** since there are 14 days in two weeks.
6. **9,000**
7. **527**
8. **185,135**
9. **3,795**
10. **$1,872**

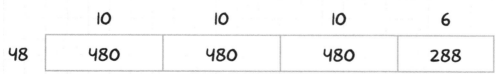

2.2.B Dividing Multi-Digit Whole Numbers

1. **C.** 345 ÷ 23 = 15
2. 24.24 × 12 = 288
3. **A.** 672 ÷ 21 = 32
4. **36**

	10	10	10	6
48	480	480	480	288

ANSWER SHEET

5. 27. 27 × 82 = 2214
6. B. 700 ÷ 20 = 35
7. 120

	100	10	10
12	1200	120	120

8. 364. 364 × 14 = 5,094
9. D. 1,088 ÷ 64 = 17
10. 113

	100	10	3
11	1100	110	33

2.2.C Add, Subtract, Multiply, and Divide Decimals

1. 22.05. It's a multiplication problem (Estimate, Line up, Multiply, Add the Decimal).
2. 5.75. It's an addition problem (Line up, Add Zeros, Add).
3. 22.8. It's a division problem (Move the Decimal, Divide).
4. 161.80. It's a subtraction problem (Line up, Add Zeros, Subtract).
5. 31.25. It's a multiplication problem (Estimate, Line up, Multiply, Add the Decimal).
6. 18.57. It's an addition problem (Line up, Add Zeros, Add).
7. $295.50. It's a subtraction problem (Line up, Add Zeros, Subtract).
8. 8.75. It's a division problem (Estimate, Move the Decimal, Divide).
9. $57.75. It's a subtraction problem (Line up, Add Zeros, Subtract).
10. 61.1. It's an addition problem (Line up, Add Zeros, Add).

2.3. Chapter Test

1. $3.00. It's a multiplication problem (Estimate, Line up, Multiply, Add the Decimal).
2. B. The 8 in 175.879 is to the left of the 8 in 75.789, which means it is 10 times the value.
3. 5,096. Use an area model to find the product.

4. A. Rewrite the numbers in standard form. $3.75 \times 10^2 = 375$ and $8.9 \times 10^1 = 89$.
5. C. Place value shifts to the left four times.
6. 14. It's a division problem. Use an area model to find the quotient.
7. $76.40. This is a two-step problem. First, multiply 2×26.25. Then subtract the product from 128.90.

8. $(1 \times 10) + (7 \times \dfrac{1}{10}) + (5 \times \dfrac{1}{100}) + (4 \times \dfrac{1}{1000})$. Multiply each digit by its place value.

9. 3.2. It's a division problem (Estimate, Move the Decimal, Divide).
10. 3,100. It's a mulitplication problem (25×124).
11. A. Place value shifts one time to the right.
12. $0.75. It's a subtraction problem (Line up, Add Zeros, Subtract).
13. B. Place value shifts two times to the left.
14. C. The numbers are equal. The zero after the decimal does not cahnge the value of the number.
15. A. The place value shifts one place to the right.
16. B. 71.5 rounds up to 72.
17. 1.70. The number to the right is greater than 4 so you round up.
18. 336. It's a multiplication problem (16×21).
19. D. The other numbers are greater than or equal to 5.09.
20. 128. Use an area model to find the quotient.

Chapter 3:

3.1.A Add and Subtract Fractions with Unlike Denominators

1. $1\dfrac{1}{12}$ or $\dfrac{13}{12}$. The common denominator is 12.

2. $2\dfrac{3}{4}$ or $\dfrac{11}{4}$. The common denominator is 4.

3. $3\dfrac{1}{3}$ or $\dfrac{10}{3}$. The common denominator is 6.

4. $1\dfrac{11}{16}$ or $\dfrac{27}{16}$. The common denominator is 16.

5. $3\frac{1}{10}$ or $\frac{31}{10}$. The common denominator is 10.

6. $4\frac{1}{3}$ or $\frac{13}{12}$. The common denominator is 6.

7. $\frac{2}{3}$. The common denominator is 12.

8. $\frac{1}{14}$. The common denominator is 14.

9. $1\frac{2}{3}$ or $\frac{5}{3}$. The common denominator is 9.

10. $1\frac{1}{2}$ or $\frac{3}{2}$. The common denominator is 6.

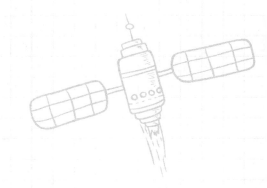

3.1.B Solve Word Problems Involving Addition and Subtraction of Fractions

1. She drank $\frac{1}{2}$ of the water in her water bottle.

   The equation is $\frac{1}{3} + \frac{1}{6} = \frac{3}{6}$.

2. C. It's a subtraction problem. The difference between the total miles needed and the miles already walked, will result in the number of miles he has left.

3. 4. The equation is $5\frac{1}{6} - 1\frac{1}{6}$.

4. A. It's an addition problem.

5. $8\frac{1}{2}$. The equation can be expressed $3\frac{2}{3} + 4\frac{5}{6}$.

6. B. We can tell it's wrong without calculating because we know that $\frac{3}{4}$ is larger than $\frac{1}{2}$.

7. $\frac{13}{20}$ apples. The equation can be expressed $\frac{2}{5} + \frac{1}{4}$. The common denominator is 20.

8. $\frac{9}{10}$. The equation can be expressed $2\frac{1}{2} - 1\frac{3}{5}$. The common denominator is 10.

9. $4\frac{1}{3}$. The equation can be expressed $6\frac{5}{6} - 2\frac{1}{2}$. The common denominator is 6.

10. False. We know that $\frac{1}{2}$ is smaller than $\frac{3}{4}$. The answer must be incorrect because we are adding to $\frac{3}{4}$.

11. $12\frac{2}{5}$ hours. The common denominator is 10. It's an addition problem.

12. C. It's an addtion problem. The common denominator is 12.

13. $\frac{7}{16}$ pounds. It's an addition problem. The common denominator is 16.

14. $4\frac{1}{4}$ ounces. It's an addition problem.

15. $12\frac{5}{6}$ yards. It's an addition problem.

16. $\frac{10}{15}$ of her money.

17. $2\frac{1}{4}$ gallons. It's a subtractinon problem. The common denominator is 8.

18. $3\frac{1}{6}$ feet. It's a subtractinon problem. The common denominator is 6.

19. $\frac{4}{9}$. It's an addition problem. The common denominator is 9.

20. $\frac{3}{4}$ hour. It's a subtraction problem. The common denominator is 4.

3.2.A Dividing with Fractions - Part 1

1. $\frac{3}{4}$. 3 cupcakes divided by 4 people.

2. C. You can solve the problem using number sense. We know that $3 \times 2 = 6$. We also know that $3 \times 1 = 3$. So, we know that the answer is between 1 and 2. The only answer choice that works is C.

3. $\frac{7}{2}$. 7 cookies divided by 2 people.

4. C. You can solve the problem using number sense. We know that $8 \times 10 = 80$. We also know that $8 \times 9 = 72$. So, we know that the answer is between 9 and 10. The only answer choice that works is B.

5. $\frac{36}{4}$. 36 ounces divided by 4 people.

6. C. You can solve the problem using number sense. We know that $5 \times 2 = 10$. We also know that $5 \times 3 = 15$. So, we know that the answer is between 2 and 3. The only answer choice that works is C.

7. A. If each person got two candy bars, she would need 22 candy bars (11×2). If each person got one candy bar, she would have several left over (11×1). The answer will fall somewhere in between these two numbers.

8. C. If each person had 3 ounces of punch, the would have several ounces leftover (6×3). If each person had 4 ounces of juice, he would need 4 more ounces of juice (6×4). The answer will fall between these two numbers.

9. A. If each person gets 1 bag of candy, then Daneel would have some leftover (4×1). If each person gets 2 bags of candy, Daneel would need 3 more bags of candy (4×2). The answer will fall between these two numbers.

10. B. She would have slime leftover if she gave each classmate 3 ounces (9×2). She would need more slime if she wanted to give each classmate 3 ounces (9×3).

3.2.B Multiplying with Fractions

1. $\frac{5}{4}$ or $1\frac{1}{4}$. Rewrite the equation as $\frac{5}{1} \times \frac{1}{4}$

2. $\frac{18}{3}$ or 6. Rewrite the equation as $\frac{2}{3} \times \frac{9}{1}$

3. $\frac{35}{12}$ or $2\frac{11}{12}$. Rewrite the equation as $\frac{7}{1} \times \frac{5}{12}$

4. $\frac{9}{2}$ or $4\frac{1}{2}$. Rewrite the equation as $\frac{9}{1} \times \frac{1}{2}$

5. $\frac{9}{4}$ or $2\frac{1}{4}$. Rewrite the equation as $\frac{3}{1} \times \frac{3}{4}$

6. $\frac{12}{3}$ or 4. Rewrite the equation as $\frac{6}{1} \times \frac{2}{3}$

7. $\frac{10}{6}$ or $1\frac{2}{3}$. Rewrite the equation as $\frac{2}{1} \times \frac{5}{6}$

8. $\frac{12}{4}$ or 3. Rewrite the equation as $\frac{4}{1} \times \frac{3}{4}$

9. $\frac{6}{5}$ or $1\frac{1}{5}$. Rewrite the equation as $\frac{3}{1} \times \frac{2}{5}$

10. $\frac{7}{2}$ or $3\frac{1}{2}$. Rewrite the equation as $\frac{1}{2} \times \frac{7}{1}$

11. B. Count the units down
12. C. Count the units across
13. C. Area = length × width
14. C. Count the units down
15. B. Count the units across
16. C. Area = length × width

17. $12\frac{1}{2}$ units². Multiply $2\frac{1}{2}$ by 5

18. 18 units². Multiply $4\frac{1}{2}$ by 4

19. 45.5 units². Multiply 7 by $6\frac{1}{2}$

20. $4\frac{2}{3}$ units². Multiply $2\frac{1}{3}$ by 2

3.2.C Multiplying to Scale

1. $\frac{1}{2}$ is scaled up. Multiplying a number by a fraction **greater than 1** results in a product greater than the original number.

2. **2** is scaled down. Multiplying a number by a fraction **less than 1** results in a product smaller than the original number.

3. C. $\frac{3}{2}$ is greater than 1

4. C. $\frac{3}{3}$ is equal to 1

5. B. $\frac{7}{8}$ is less than 1

6. **2** is scaled up. Multiplying a number by a fraction **greater than 1** results in a product greater than the original number.

7. A. $\frac{3}{5}$ is less than 1

8. C. $\frac{3}{4}$ is less than 1

9. Scaled down. Multiplying a number by a fraction **less than 1** results in a product smaller than the original number.

10. C. Multiplying a number by a fraction **greater than 1** results in a product greater than the original number.

11. Scaled up. Multiplying a number by a fraction **greater than 1** results in a product greater than the original number.

12. C. $\frac{12}{9}$ is greater than 1

13. C. $\frac{5}{6}$ is less than 1

14. C. $\frac{5}{8}$ is less than 1

15. C. $\frac{2}{1}$ is greater than 1 Which expression is greater than $\frac{8}{9}$? Select your answer without multiplying.

16. C. $\frac{7}{7}$ is equal to 1

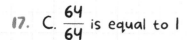
17. C. $\dfrac{64}{64}$ is equal to 1

18. C. $\dfrac{1}{2}$ is less than 1

19. C. $\dfrac{9}{8}$ is greater than 1

20. B. $\dfrac{1}{2}$ is less than 1

3.2.D Solve Real World Problems Involving Multiplication of Fractions

1. $\dfrac{15}{32}$ feet. Multiply $3\dfrac{3}{4}$ by $\dfrac{1}{8}$

2. $\dfrac{14}{3}$ miles or $4\dfrac{2}{3}$ miles. Multiply 7 by $\dfrac{2}{3}$

3. $\dfrac{3}{8}$ pounds. Multiply $\dfrac{1}{2}$ by $\dfrac{3}{4}$

4. $26\dfrac{2}{3}$ ounces. Multiply 32 by $\dfrac{5}{6}$

5. $\dfrac{80}{15}$ or $5\dfrac{1}{3}$. Multiply $6\dfrac{2}{3}$ by $\dfrac{4}{5}$

6. $1\dfrac{11}{20}$. Multiply $6\dfrac{1}{5}$ by $\dfrac{1}{4}$

7. $\dfrac{5}{6}$. Multiply $2\dfrac{1}{2}$ by $\dfrac{1}{3}$

8. 3 boxes. Multiply 12 by $\dfrac{1}{4}$

9. $1\dfrac{5}{6}$ hours. Multiply $5\dfrac{1}{2}$ by $\dfrac{1}{3}$

10. $1\dfrac{5}{8}$. Multiply 13 by $\dfrac{1}{8}$

3.2.E Dividing Fractions - Part II

1. A. $\frac{1}{2} \div 6$ is the same as $\frac{1}{2} \times \frac{1}{6}$, which equals $\frac{1}{12}$.

2. B. Represent 6 with a drawing of six separate units. Divide each unit in half. Count the number of halves to determine the answer.

3. B. $\frac{3}{4} \div 3$ is the same as $\frac{3}{4} \times \frac{1}{3}$, which equals $\frac{3}{12}$ or $\frac{1}{4}$.

4. A. Represent 3 with a drawing. Divide each unit into fourths. Group the fourths into groups of three, and then count the groups.

5. A. $\frac{7}{8} \div 7$ is the same as $\frac{7}{8} \times \frac{1}{7}$, which equals $\frac{7}{42}$ or $\frac{1}{8}$.

6. B. Represent 7 with a drawing. Divide each unit into eighths. Group the eighths into groups of seven, and then count the groups.

7. A. $\frac{5}{9} \div 5$ is the same as $\frac{5}{9} \times \frac{1}{5}$, which equals $\frac{5}{45}$ or $\frac{1}{9}$.

8. B. Represent 5 with a drawing. Divide each unit into ninths. Group the ninths into groups of five, and then count the groups.

9. B. Represent 2 with a drawing. Divide each unit into fifths. Group the fifths into groups of three, and then count the groups.

10. A. $\frac{3}{5} \div 2$ is the same as $\frac{3}{5} \times \frac{1}{2}$, which equals $\frac{3}{10}$.

11. $1\frac{11}{14}$ ounces. The equation is $12\frac{1}{2} \div 7$, which equals $1\frac{11}{14}$.

12. 12. The equation is $6 \div \frac{1}{2}$, which equals 12.

13. $6\frac{3}{16}$. The equation is $24\frac{3}{4} \div 4$, which equals $6\frac{3}{16}$.

14. $\frac{17}{40}$. The equation is $2\frac{1}{8} \div 5$ which equals $\frac{17}{40}$.

15. $2\frac{5}{8}$. The equation is $5\frac{1}{4} \div 2$, which equals $2\frac{5}{8}$.

16. 36. The equation is $9 \div \frac{1}{4}$, which equals 36.

17. $1\frac{1}{2}$. The equation is $6 \div 4$, which equals $1\frac{1}{2}$.

18. $8\frac{1}{8}$. The equation is $32\frac{1}{2} \div 4$, which equals $8\frac{1}{8}$.

19. $5\frac{1}{4}$. The equation is $15\frac{3}{4} \div 3$, which equals $5\frac{1}{4}$.

20. 18. The equation is $3 \div \frac{1}{6}$, which equals 18.

3.3. Chapter Test

1. $\frac{11}{4}$ or $2\frac{3}{4}$. It's a subtraction problem Subtract $\frac{3}{4}$ from $3\frac{1}{2}$.

2. $\frac{10}{6}$ or $1\frac{2}{3}$. It's a division problem. Divide 10 by 6.

3. Scaled down. $\frac{1}{2}$ is less than 1.

4. A. $\frac{1}{2}$ is less than 1.

5. $6\frac{2}{3}$ servings. 5 needs to be divided by $\frac{3}{4}$. Use a model to find the answer.

6. $\frac{6}{5}$ miles or $1\frac{1}{5}$ miles. Multiply 3 by $\frac{2}{5}$ Leo runs 3 miles.

7. 2. $\frac{8}{1} \times \frac{1}{4} = \frac{8}{4}$. Multiply across.

8. $\frac{25}{8}$ or $3\frac{1}{8}$.

9. $\frac{16}{3}$ or $5\frac{1}{3}$

10. B. $\frac{3}{4}$ is less than 1.

11. $9\frac{7}{12}$

    Add $5\frac{5}{6}$ to $3\frac{3}{4}$. The common denominator is 24.

12. $\frac{7}{24}$

    Divided $3\frac{1}{2}$ by 12 people.

13. 7 feet

    Multiply 8 by $\frac{7}{8}$.

14. $\frac{43}{18}$ or $2\frac{7}{18}$

    The common denominator is 18. $\frac{7}{2} - \frac{10}{9}$.

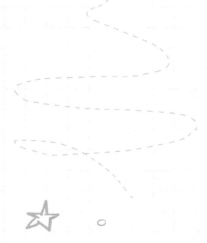

15. $\frac{27}{8}$ or $3\frac{3}{8}$

    Multiply across. Check your answer with a model.

16. B

    There are too many cookies for each person to only have 2 (5 × 2 = 10) and there aren't enough cookies for each person to have 3 (5 × 3 = 15).

17. $\frac{21}{8}$ or $2\frac{5}{8}$

    Subtract $\frac{1}{8}$ from $2\frac{3}{4}$.

18. C

    Count the units down.

19. B
Count the units across.

20. C
Area = length × width $(4 × 3\frac{3}{4})$

   A. 14

   B. $14\frac{3}{4}$

   C. 15

Chapter 4:

4.1. Convert like Measurement Units

1. **82** ounces
First convert cups to ounces (16 × 8 = 128). Next subtract 46 from 128 (128 - 46 = 82).

2. **2,700** seconds
Convert minutes to seconds (45 × 60 = 2700).

3. **128** ounces
Multiply 8 by 16 since each pound has 16 ounces.

4. **D**
First multiply 3 by $\frac{1}{4}$ to find out how many miles Alyssa still needs to run. Then convert miles into feet by multiplying the answer by **5,280**.

5. **156**
Multiply 3 by **52** since there are **52** weeks in each year.

6. **984** ounces. First multiply 123 by $\frac{1}{2}$ to find out how much his brother weighs in pounds. Then multiply the answer by **16** since each pound has 16 ounces.

7. $2\frac{1}{4}$ feet. First divide 3 by 4. Then multiply the answer by 3 since each yard is 3 feet.

8. 3. It takes 2 cups to make 1 pint. Divide 6 by 2.

9. D. Subtract 16 by 12 to determine how many more kilometers her friend biked. Multiply the answer by 1,000 since there is 1,000 kilometers in each meter.

10. 3. Divide 6,000 by 2,000.

4.2 Represent and Interpret Data

1.

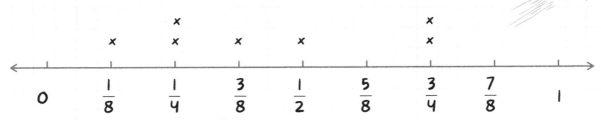

Break the number line into $\frac{1}{8}$ section. Simplify and plot each fraction.

2. B. Simplify each fraction to determine its place on the line plot.

3.

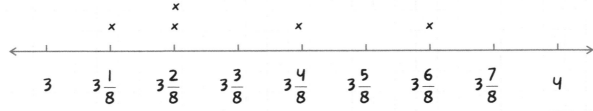

Break the number line into $\frac{1}{8}$ section. Simplify and plot each fraction.

4. $\frac{5}{8}$. The tallest student is $3\frac{3}{4}$ ft tall. The shortest student is $3\frac{1}{8}$ ft tall. Subtract $3\frac{1}{8}$ from $3\frac{3}{4}$.

5. $7\frac{1}{4}$ feet tall. The two tallest students are $3\frac{3}{4}$ ft and $3\frac{1}{2}$ feet. Add $3\frac{3}{4}$ to $3\frac{1}{2}$ to find the total height.

6. B. $3\frac{1}{4}$ ft appears on the line plot more than the other numbers.

7. C. $3\frac{3}{4}$ is the largest plot on the number line. It is simplified as $3\frac{1}{2}$.

8. B. $2\frac{1}{4}$ is the smallest plot on the number line.

9. The chicks weigh $22\frac{3}{4}$ ounces all together. Add all of the plots together $(2\frac{1}{4}) + (3 \times 2\frac{1}{2}) + (3) + (2 \times 3\frac{1}{4}) + 3\frac{1}{2}$.

10. $2\frac{27}{32}$ ounces. Take the total weight calculated in question 9 ($22\frac{3}{4}$ ounces) and divide is by 8.

4.3.A Understanding Volume

1. 16. There are 2 rows of 8 cubes.
2. 32. There are 4 rows of 8 cubes.
3. 6 cubes. One cube is completely hidden but we know it is holding the top cube up.
4. 5 cubes. Two cubes on top, three cubes on bottom.
5. 20 cubes. 2 rows of 10 cubes each.
6. 40. Count the bottom row and fill in one row on top.
7. 36. Count the bottom row and fill in two rows on top.
8. 75. Count the bottom row and fill in four rows on top.
9. 24. Count the bottom row and fill in three rows on top.
10. 32. Count the bottom row and fill in three rows on top.
11. B. Each cube represents one cubic unit.
12. B. Each cube represents one cubic unit.
13. B. Each cube represents one cubic unit.
14. 4. There are two cubes on the bottom and two layers.
15. 6. There are two cubes on the bottom and three layers.
16. 120. There are ten cubes on the bottom and twelve layers.
17. 65. There are thirteen cubes on the bottom and 5 layers.
18. 12. There are four cubes on the bottom and three layers.
19. 63. There are seven cubes on the bottom and nine layers.
20. 12. There are twelve cubes on the bottom and one layer.

4.3.B Measuring Volume by Counting

1. 100 cm³. The base has **20** cubes and there are **5** layers.
2. 24 cm³. The base has **8** cubes and there are **3** layers.
3. 45 cm³. The base has **15** cubes and there are **3** layers.
4. 55 cm³. Subtract **45** cm³ from **100** cm³.
5. 69 cm³. Add **24** cm³ to **45** cm³.
6. C. Figure A has a volume of **16** in³ Figure B has a volume of **30** in³ and Figure C has a volume of **32** in³.
7. A. Figure A has a volume of **16** ft³ Figure B has a volume of **30** ft³ and Figure C has a volume of **24** ft³.
8. 16 in³. Subtract **16** in³ from **32** in³.
9. 78 in³. Add **16** in³, **30** in³, and **32** in³.
10. Answers may vary but should contain **6** cubes with the measurement in feet.

4.3.C Find the volume of a right rectangular prism

1. 56. Multiply base by height.
2. 90. Multiply length by width by height.
3. 8. Multiply length by width by height.
4. 34. Subtract **56** from **90**.
5. 30 cm³. 5 × 6 × 1
6. C. 20 × 10 × 5
7. 120 cm³. 40 × 3
8. 110 ft³. (2 × 11) + (3 × 11) × 2
9. 36 ft³. (2 × 3) + (5 × 3 × 2)
10. 150. 25 × 6
11. C. 12 × 2 × 1 = 24
12. A. Multiply the length and width. Divide the volume by the product.
13. B. 10 × 11 × 1 = 110
14. B. Multiply the length and width. Divide the volume by the product.
15. C. 18 × 3 × 1 = 54. The units should be in feet.
16. 84 ft³. 12 × 7
17. 176 ft³. 11 × 2 × 8

18. 44 ft³. 11 × 1 × 4
19. 132 ft³. 176 - 44
20. 304 ft³. 176 + 44 + 84

4.4. Chapter Test

1. 640. Multiply 5 by 128 since there are 128 ounces in each gallon.
2. 27 feet. Multiply yards by feet (9 × 3).
3. C. First subtract 2 from 3 to find the distance in miles. Then convert miles to feet by multiplying the answer by 5,280.
4. B. Multiply 3 by 8 since there are 8 ounces in each cup.
5. 15,840 ft. First subtract 2 from 5 to see how many miles he has left to run. Then convert miles to feet.

6. $\frac{7}{8}$ inches. Subtract the shortest length from the longest length to find the difference ($2\frac{7}{8}$ - 2).

7. $8\frac{3}{8}$ inches. Add the three longest lengths together ($2\frac{6}{8}$ + $2\frac{6}{8}$ + $2\frac{7}{8}$).

8. 2.4. Add all the data points together (24) and divide that number by 10.

9. $\frac{1}{4}$ inches. Multiply the shortest length (2 inches) by $\frac{1}{8}$.

10. The boxes have the same volume, 10 cubic centimeters.

11. 36. Find the volume of both boxes. Add them together.
12. 5 cubes. Count the cubes.
13. 6 cubic units. Count the cubes. Check your label.
14. 9 cubic units. Count the cubes. Check your label.
15. 3 cubic units. Figure 3 has 3 more cubes than figure 2.
16. 2 cubic units. Multiply length times width times height.
17. 15 cubic units. Multiply base times height.

18. **6** cubic units. Multiply base times height.
19. **B.** Figure **2** has the largest volume.
20. **7** cubic centimeters smaller. Subtract the volume of figure **3** from the volume of figure **2** (15 - 6).

Chapter 5:

5.1.A Defining a Coordinate System

1. C. Point A is on the y-axis. Its coordinates are (**0, 5**).
2. B. Point B is on the x-axis. Its coordinates are (**4, 0**).
3. D. Point A represents the origin, but it is also where the x-axis and y-axis intersect. Therefore, it is on all three.
4. B. The point is up **2**.
5. A. The point is over **4**.
6. A. The point is up **1**.
7. B. The point is over **2**.
8. (**0, 6**). Over **0** on the x-axis, Up **6** on the y-axis.
9. (**4, 4**). Over **4** on the x-axis, Up **4** on the y-axis.
10. (**2, 0**). Over **2** on the x-axis, Up **0** on the y-axis.
11. (**4, 0**). Over **4** on the x-axis, Up **0** on the y-axis.
12. (**0, 3**). Over **0** on the x-axis, Up **3** on the y-axis.
13. (**2, 2**). Over **2** on the x-axis, Up **2** on the y-axis.
14. (**8, 2**). Over **8** on the x-axis, Up **2** on the y-axis.
15. (**2, 8**). Over **2** on the x-axis, Up **8** on the y-axis.

5.1.B Graphing Points

1.

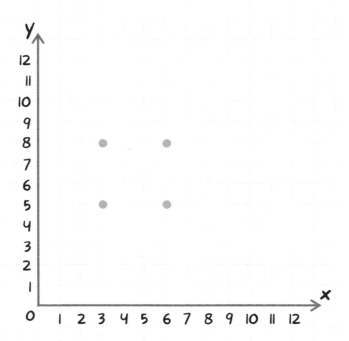

2. **3** units
3. B. Count the number of units that fall in between the two points.
4. B. Count the number of units that fall in between the points. Emanual lives **2** units (or miles) from Simon.
5. A. Count the number of units that fall in between the points. Or, subtract the Joe's y-coordinate from Simon's y-coordinate. Joe lives **8** units (or miles) from Simon.
6. A. Count the number of units that fall in between the points. Or, subtract Simon's y-coordinates from Emanuel's y-coordinate. Emanuel lives **2** units (or miles) from Simon.
7. A. Vera has only grown 1 inch.
8. C. Daniel grew **2** inches. Samantha grew **5** inches.
9. C. 1 + 2 + 3 + 5 = 11.
10. A. Most of the points are plotted at **8** on the x-axis.
11. D. Daniel is **9**. The rest of the students are **8**.

12.

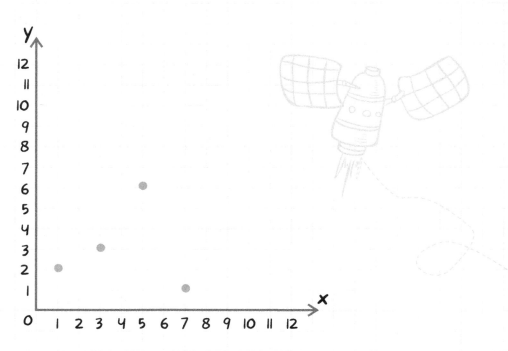

13. 12. Add all of the y-coordinates (2 + 3 + 6 + 1).
14. 3. Find **3** on the *x*-axis. Then locate where the point lands on the y-axis.
15. 5. The largest plot has a y-coordinate of **6**. The *x*-coordinate for this point is **5**.

5.2.A Understanding attributes of two-dimensional figures.

1. C. See chart from overview.
2. B. See chart from overview.
3. B. See chart from overview.
4. A. See chart from overview.
5. C. See chart from overview.
6. Answers may vary. Shapes should have 4 straight sides.
7. Answers may vary. Shapes should have fewer than 4 sides or sides that are not straight.
8. Answers may vary. Shapes should have 4 sides and the opposite sides should be parallel.
9. Answers may vary. Shapes should have fewer than 4 sides or opposite sides that are not parallel.
10. Answers may vary. Shapes should have less than 3 sides. For example, a circle would be an acceptable response.

5.2.B Classifying two-dimensional figures

1. A. A square is a special kind of rectangle. It has four sides with equal angles.
2. B. A square can be a rhombus, but not all rhombuses are squares.
3. B. A rectangle can be a parallelogram, but not all parallelograms are rectangles.
4. Shape 2 and 3.
5. Shape 3. Two of its sides are not parallel.
6. Polygon. See chart from overview.
7. Trapezoid. See chart from overview.
8. Rectangle. See chart from overview.
9. Square. See chart from overview.
10. Answers may vary. Response should reflect the same hierarchy presented in the chart from overview.

5.3. Chapter Test

1.

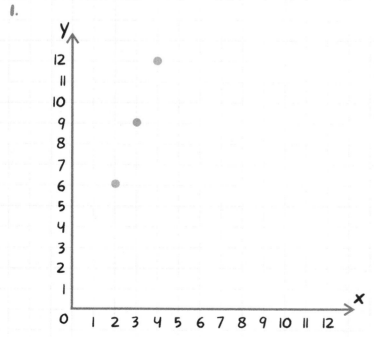

The x-coordinate is given. To find the y-coordinate, you need to multiply each x-coordinate by 3. (2 × 3), (3 × 3), and (4 × 3)

2.

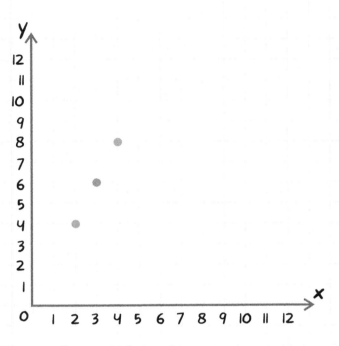

The x-coordinate is given. To find the y-coordinate, you need to multiply each x-coordinate by **2**. (2 × 2), (3 × 2), and (4 × 2)

3.

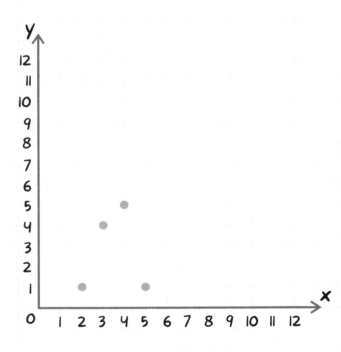

4. C. At 4 he ran 5 miles (4 has the largest y-coordinate).
5. 3 miles. He ran 4 miles at 3 and he ran 1 mile at 5 (4 - 1 = 3).
6. 11 miles. Add all of the miles (1 + 4 + 5 + 1 = 11).
7. B. He runs 1 mile at both 2 and 5. The numbers have the same y-coordinate.
8. 8
9. 8
10. 3. The points are 3 units apart.

11.  They have 4 sides and four equal angles.

12. 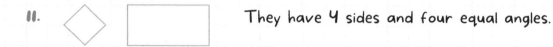 They have 4 sides.

13. 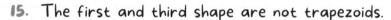 It has more than one parallel side.

14. ◯ It has no sides.

15. The first and third shape are not trapezoids.
16. B. All of the shapes are polygons.
17. C. A trapezoid is a quadrilateral and a square, but none of the other shapes are trapezoids.
18. C. A rectangle is a parallelogram, quadrilateral and polygon.
19. C. A square is a rectangle, parallelogram, quadrilateral and polygon.
20. Answers will vary, but should align with the hierarchy chart provided.
    A square always has four sides.

Chapter 6: Mixed Assessment

1. **56.** First calculate 16 - 3. Then add 1. Then multiply by 4.

2. **2.6** miles. Multiply 13 by $\frac{1}{5}$.

3. **B.** Operations in parenthesis should be calculated first.

4. **A.** First calculate **5 - 3.** Then add **1.** Then multiply by **2.** Then add **6.** The answer to the equation is **12.**

5. **12 + (8 × 5).** You need to multiply 8 by 5 in order to add twelve to the product.

6. **$6.25.** Multiply 1.25 by 5

7. **B.** The 8 is in the tenths place.

8. **B.** Multiply **24.50** by **3.** Then add **32.25** to the product. Then subtract the sum from **164.75.**

9. $1\frac{11}{16}$. Subtract $\frac{1}{16}$ from $1\frac{3}{4}$

10. **22.** Multiply base times height for the first two pacakges. Multiply length by width by height for the third package. Add all of the products together.

11. **26,400** ft. First subtract **5** from **10** to see how many miles he has left. Then convert miles to feet by multiplying the difference by **5280.**

12. **256** ounces. Divide **6** by **3** to get **2** gallons for each class. Then convert **2** gallons to ounces by multiplying **2** by **128.**

13. **156** weeks. Multiply **52** by **3.**

14. **5** cups. Convert cups to ounces by multiplying **5** by **8.** She needs **40** ounces for her recipe. Subtract **40** from **80** to see how many ounces she will have left. Then convert **40** ounces to cups by dividing **40** by **8.**

15. **10.** I ton equals **2,000** pounds. So, divide **2,000** by **200** to see how many pandas will fit on each vehicle.

16. $4\frac{5}{8}$. The common denominator is 8.

17. $\frac{2}{5}$. Multiply across and simplify.

18. The presents have the same volume. Length multiplied by width.

19. The original equation is multiplied by **3**. The new equation is **3** times larger.

20. B. 12 is less than 99.
21. C. The zero in the thousandths place doesn't change the value of the number.
22. B. When multiplying by a value less than 1, the number decreases.
23. A. $1.89 \times 10^2 = 189$. $12 \times 10 = 120$.

24. $(1 \times 100) + (2 \times 10) + (1 \times 1) + (1 \times \frac{1}{10})$. Multiply each digit by its place value.

25. 6.3
26. A. The place value shift one place to the right.
27. 4. Whole numbers do not have decimals. Since the tenths place is greater than 5 round up.
28. 224 laps. Multiply **32** by **7**.

29. $1\frac{1}{4}$. Divide 15 by 12.

30. 9. Divide 6 by $\frac{2}{3}$.

31.

Hours Reading	Screen Time
3	1
6	2
9	3
12	4

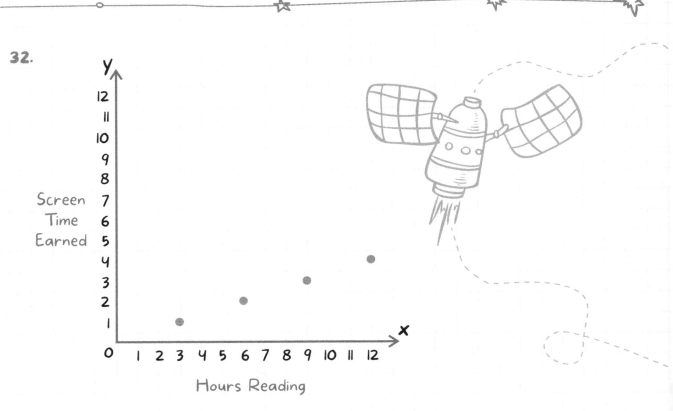

32.

33. y = x ÷ 3. For every one hour of screen time, Isabella needs to read 3 hours.

34. 5 hours. She will have read for 3 more hours, which earns her another hour of screen time.

35. 12.

36. $\frac{7}{8}$ inches

37. $\frac{2}{8}$. Use the line plot as a number line and count the spaces in between.

38. 3. Look at $\frac{1}{2}$ on the line plot and count the x's.

39. 4 $\frac{1}{8}$ inches. Add all of the plots.

40. Chocolate. Chocolate is $2 for every scoop. Vanilla is $1 for every scoop.

41. C. Chocolate is $2 for every 1 scoop.

42. y = x. Vanilla is $1 for every 1 scoop.

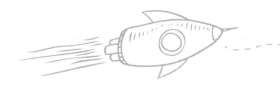

43. B. Chocolate is twice as much as Vanilla.
44. $4. 3 scoops of chocolate is $6. Subtract 6 from 10.
45. $4. 2 scoops of vanilla is $2. 1 scoop of chocolate is $2. Add the prices together.

46. $(7 \times \frac{1}{10}) + (8 \times \frac{1}{100}) + (9 \times \frac{1}{1000})$. Multiply each digit by its place value.

47. $(1 \times 10) + (3 \times \frac{1}{10})$. Multiply each digit by its place value.

48. Figure B. Figure B has a volume of 32 cm³.
49. 86 cm³. 24 cm³ + 32 cm³ + 30 cm³.
50. 6 cm³. 30 cm³ - 24 cm³.
51. Answers may vary. Model should have fewer than 32 blocks.
52. C. First add 12 to 2. Then divide by 2.

53. $\frac{6}{8}$ or $\frac{3}{4}$

54. 8,160. It's a muliplication problem. Multiply 240 by 34.
55. C. Place value shifts to the left three times.
56. B. Figure B has an volume of 3 × 3 × 10 = 90 ft³.
57. A. Figure A has a volume of 4 × 1 × 2 = 8 ft³.
58. 27 ft³. Subtract 8 from 35.
59. 133 ft³. 8 + 90 + 35 = 133 ft³.
60. Answers may vary. Volume should be greater than 90 cm³ Should have length, width and height labeled OR base and heigh labled.
61. 8. Divide 148 by 18.
62. 42

	10	10	10	10	2
24	240	240	240	240	48

ANSWER SHEET

63. B. Multiply 16 times $\frac{1}{8}$.

64. 8. The number to the right of the tenths place is greater than 5 so we round up.

65. $1\frac{1}{6}$. Multiply $3\frac{1}{2}$ by $\frac{1}{3}$.

66. B. Each number is represented by place value.
67. 1,500. Place value shifts to the left once.
68. 25. Place value shifts to the left once.
69. A. Count units going up.
70. B. Count units across.
71. 17. Count all units OR multiply length by width.
72. A. Count units going up.
73. C. Count units going across.

74. 5. Count all units.

75.

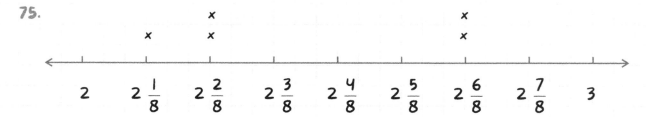

76. $\frac{5}{8}$. Use the line plot as a number line. Count the spaces between.

77. $12\frac{1}{8}$. Add the lengths together.

78. $2\frac{17}{40}$. Divide $12\frac{1}{8}$ by 5.

79. $(1 \times 10) + (4 \times \frac{1}{10}) + (5 \times \frac{1}{100})$. Multiply each digit by its place value.

80. D. Multiply the original expression by 6. Use brackets to keep the original expression together.

81. 4836. 13 multiplied by 403.
82. 1,260. 105 multiplied by 12.
83. 2,025. 135 multiplied by 15.
84. B. Line up the decimals and add.
85. C. 5 laps of backstroke plus 4 laps of freestyle. Multilpied by 4 days a week.
86. 56.7

87. $1\frac{5}{6}$ hours. $5\frac{1}{2}$ multiplied by $\frac{1}{3}$.

88. $1\frac{1}{12}$. The common denominator is 12.

89. 407.7. Line up the decimals and subtract.
90. Shape 1. Its has 4 sides and angles that are equal.
91. Shape 2. It's lines are not straight.
92. B. A square can be a rhombus, but a rhombus is not always a square because it's angles do not have to be equal.
93. C. A circle has no sides. A polygon must have at least three sides.
94. A. A rhombus has 4 equal sides. A square always has 4 equal sides.
95. C. A triangle never has parallel sides.
96. Scaled Down. When multiplied by less than 1 whole numbers scale down.

97. C. $\frac{2}{1}$ is greater than 1.

98. $7\frac{4}{5}$. Multiply 13 by $\frac{3}{5}$.

99. $13\frac{1}{2}$. Muliply across then simplify.

100. $6\frac{1}{8}$. The common denominator is 8.

Made in the USA
Coppell, TX
06 June 2020